We come with this place

For Gudanji
This is for you … so you know
why your feet walk the path they do
why your eyes seek the shadows
why your ears hear the stories running in the air
whispering tastes into your mouth to then
nourish your body.

This is for you so you will know the stories
when they walk with you
and talk in their many voices
so, listen with all of who you are and feel this story
running through your body …
taking you into country.
Mankujba!

We come with this place

Debra Dank

echo

echo

Echo Publishing
An imprint of Bonnier Books UK
4th Floor, Victoria House, Bloomsbury Square
London WC1B 4DA
www.echopublishing.com.au
www.bonnierbooks.co.uk

Echo Publishing acknowledges the traditional custodians of Country
throughout Australia. We recognise their continuing connection to land,
sea and waters. We pay our respects to Elders past and present.

First Nations peoples are advised that this book contains names of deceased
people, and content that may be considered culturally sensitive.

First published 2022

Printed and bound in Australia by Griffin Press, part of Ovato

MIX
Paper from
responsible sources
FSC® C009448

The paper this book is printed on is certified against the Forest Stewardship
Council® Standards. Griffin Press holds chain of custody certification
SGSHK-COC-005088. FSC® promotes environmentally responsible, socially
beneficial and economically viable management of the world's forests.

Cover artwork and internal illustrations copyright ©
nardurna – artist, illustrator, designer | nardurna@nardurna
Specially commissioned artwork, cover design
and creative direction: nardurna@nardurna
Page design and typesetting by Shaun Jury

NATIONAL
LIBRARY
OF AUSTRALIA
A catalogue entry for this book is available from the
National Library of Australia

ISBN: 9781760687397 (paperback)
ISBN: 9781760687403 (ebook)

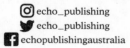

echo_publishing
echo_publishing
echopublishingaustralia

Dedication

This is for Maxine and Lurick Sowden,
my mum and my dad,
who taught me the biggest lessons in life,
and for my grandmother, Pbirrianjulunga,
who made everything possible.

About the author

Debra Dank is a Gudanji/Wakaja woman, married to
Rick, with three adult children and two granddaughters.
An educator, she has worked in teaching and learning for
many years – a gift given through the hard work of her
parents. She continues to experience the privilege of living
with Country and with family. Debra completed her PhD
in Narrative Theory and Semiotics at Deakin University
in 2021.

Preface

Much of this book was written on Country. My husband and I took a tent and swag, a mosquito net, camping table and chairs and a small generator to keep my camera and laptop powered. Like me, my son understands the true luxury of hot water and so he wired together some kind of circuit that I would attach to a spare troopie battery in order to have a hot shower.

In the early mornings, while a little black and white bird danced at my feet as I wrote, Rick cooked mudjiga, the freshwater crayfish from our creek, for our breakfast. In the cooler times of the afternoons we walked the paths that my family have most recently walked as our children have grown, but which Gudanji have been walking for thousands of years. We caught bream and barramundi for dinner and went to sleep under the sky, watching the phases of the moon shift and control the light of the stars.

We Come with This Place is, perhaps, a strange kind of letter, written to my place – a recalling of events and activities that I and my family have experienced, in order to tell Garranjini that I remember, and I know. It is all based on real events. Some parts have been reimagined, because they happened outside my presence, and several names have been changed. Our relationship with our place, however, is genuine and lives in ways that are not easily told in English words or western ways. This book began its life as part of my PhD study. I wanted to show how story works in my community and how it has contributed to our living with country for so long. It seemed to me imperative to talk about those voices, both human and non-human, who guided Gudanji for centuries before anyone else stepped onto this land.

Note

Like all languages, those used in the south-western Gulf of Carpentaria share, borrow and mix vocabulary from multiple language groups. The words from different languages used in this narrative are included here in the ways they are currently used within my family. The peoples and languages mentioned include Garawa (people of the Northern Territory Gulf Country – east side of Borroloola approximately to the Queensland border area), Gudanji (people of the north-eastern Barkly Tableland area), Kalkadoon (people of the Mount Isa area), Wakaja (people of the southern Barkly Tableland area – from the Territory and towards the Camooweal area), Wombaya (people of the central west Barkly Tableland area) and Yanyuwa (people of the Northern Territory Gulf Country – specifically the islands off the coast from Borroloola and including Borroloola).

They are all part of my family, extended and otherwise, and I offer my gratitude and respect for their role in keeping the stories.

Foreword
Dr Tyson Yunkaporta

There are some things I just can't face, but they eat away at my insides like worms. In that regard, I'm very much the same as most people living on this continent. I avoid content about the horrors of our occupation and gradual genocide as Indigenous people. I haven't dealt with the throughline of history from the savagery of the frontier wars to the interventionist policies of today.

We are our stories. Spending time with this book is like spending time with Debra Dank herself. She's like the grannies we remember who fought battles with sticks and drew nourishment and medicine from land and waters to animate our flesh. She hurts us, digs bullets out of old wounds that never healed properly, sucks out the poison and then begins our healing with love and laughter. She does this for everybody, no matter which side of the rifle you're on.

I used to know the places Debra is writing about, and I still have the thick scars on my scalp from that time when I was a little bub. I had almost forgotten about those sticks and stones, but now they burn me again and I swear I can feel the blood running down my face. But that's just hot tears that keep coming around every time I think about Debra's grandmother and what was done.

But then there's her unconditional love running through every page, and it helps a little, but not half as much as the laughter. Deb as a princess in the school play was a story that made me laugh my cheeks off, made me laugh until I cried clean tears that fell like rain after a long drought.

I had been avoiding having that good, hard cry, but I think I really needed it.

Don't you?

Contents

Prologue: Of souls and stories

One day, a long way from home, inside the Oxford University library, when the wind outside blew bitterly cold and drizzly rain fell upon those who scurried to find shelter, I carefully breathed in the dust from a 400-year-old edition of Aristotle's *De Anima – On the Soul*. I thought that book with its fragile leather jacket was too treasured and precious for even the touch of the white gloves worn by the librarian. I tried to imagine him, Aristotle, in 350 BCE, sitting and writing the words, thinking how to record the story of souls, but I could only wonder as vague images tried to speak to me through dust motes rising from the thick pale pages. It is not easy to record the story of souls.

Our Gudanji kujiga grew here with Gudanji Country about the same time as our stories, and it was long before paper and words learned to yarn together. I don't know how our mob knew about souls, just that they did, because our stories and our kujiga live inside each other, as well as out there across our country, and inside our bodies. Those stories and our kujiga find their way then, through the black and red soil of this earth, to the goodalu within us, in moments when we know to listen to our heart. Our story comes from this country, but it does not often experience the hospitality of classrooms, libraries or bookstores.

I know because I've been in those places. I sat in the classrooms of schools in Queensland in the 1960s and 1970s and have stood in front of them, and in other places of western learning, since the 1980s, but our soul-deep stories are rarely located in those establishments. It is mainly other stories that occupy their bookshelves, told in voices that have grown in other places, voices that are new to this place and are yet to learn this country. Our stories are mostly not there; they are located somewhere that is silent and hidden, in memory that is not often visited. Some of those new voices try to tell our story but their souls do not speak the language of this place and their ears are yet to learn to hear its stories.

Like our kujiga, this black soil, red dirt and these dry brown hills and fresh water tell tales that are little parts of a big story. Many voices tell our story because we do not exist here alone, nor do we walk here without the sacrifice of others – imagine the terror and the sorrow of that kind of lone story. Imagine the sorrow of living without obligation and without reciprocity in a solitary story. So this is not a story about me, rather it is about Gudanji being, becoming and continuing.

Our story is etched into the rocks and it whispers through the trees and with our kin who are more than human. The wind tells it, sometimes strolling gently, sometimes bellowing from cavernous, dark, felt places, where eyes do not see, and only our goodalu can feel. Our stories are the memories that scratch and gnaw as we walk, and we rub shoulders with the past, but mostly our stories travel with those big freshwater rivers, always looking to find their way back to the birthing salt water but still nurturing us as we bend and drink from those same waters. Some of our tangible story can be told in words; and someday, some of it might be warmed by a soft leather book cover and beautiful marbled endpapers, like the books in the Oxford library, but it will not be our full story because that is too big for words and paper and pages. It lives with our Country.

Because our story lives and is always telling new stories alongside and with the old ones, it can never occupy pages with words that are still and solitary, breathless marks locked on paper. Our story mostly has to be lived and known, like mankujba, or way of knowing, listening, seeing, thinking, believing and feeling. If you pay attention, if you know mankujba, maybe you can know a little of this country and learn a little of its goodalu and its kujiga too.

The stories, like us, grow from the soil and the fine dirt that plays around your feet and makes the dust that rolls over the vast Gudanji and Wakaja Country. The same dust that throws itself as grit into your eyes when you don't watch it, dancing with the wind across those dry places. And when we eat the food given us by our country, through the kinship we live, we eat those stories into us too.

Stories sit in many places and they talk us into *our* place. They talk us into this land the way they did with all our old people. And when we practise obligation and reciprocity, those same stories teach us to listen to the wind playing in the grasses and the clouds making signs, because those old people are sending stories still. Listen and think and feel and see and believe carefully, all together, at the same time, and let that feeling soak into your bones. Leave it there until that story is the place that grows you – from the inside out – making your bones and body strong until it is time to return that strength to our earth.

Know this story and keep it in your body, swallow each sip of it deeply just as this country drinks in the first rains. Keep it sitting inside and hold it there because awful things are being done to our country and one day it may not be able to tell us anymore. And then, what will happen to our Country, our body?

A beginning

In the beginning, long before the stories grew and became many, three women came out of the salt water to the north-east of Gudanji Country. We call them travelling Water-women – and, sometimes, we say Mermaids.

They were birthed from the salt water into an earthy place without memory and without stories. They became the first tellers of story and, in all the places they travelled, they made stories and grew the country, and the stories became law until several hundred years ago when they became lore and this place grew sorrowful.

And sometimes I think about what that first birth was like and I get lost in the complexity of time and memory and place and life-making. Did the waters heave with the pain of childbirth to thrust forth those three Water-women or was their birth journey a gentle slip from that watery womb? Did the agony of birth create an eruption with those new lives, with pain peeling back birthing tissue where water and earth met? Maybe the arrival of these three women, whose presence has made possible all the lives since then, was simply an episode making and marking time and place and birth. I don't know but I imagine the seawater streaming from their bodies as they ventured onto the shore. That birthing, a separation from the body of water, an utter becoming, and then, as they journeyed, their travels becoming utterance that is marking and making still.

I have given birth, have pushed life from my body into this world of ours, but that first birth is almost unimaginable. I know it happened, though, because we are here.

In my mind's eye, I see those women taking their first steps — cautious, stumbling steps, wary and hesitant — into a new and unfamiliar, yet-to-be-spoken world. Did light illuminate that place, silent witness to their passage? Or perhaps there was some stranger twilight, so that the women peered into a drier, grey space surely so different from their oceanic womb.

What must it have been like to take that first gasping mouthful of air? Did they feel this same air that we bring into our bodies today? Or maybe the post-birth odour of life-sustaining saltiness was also expelled from that watery womb to give more life and to extend the lasting relationship of water and earth and life. Did they, open-mouthed, gulp in its strangeness and then struggle to swallow that first breath? Perhaps, that first time, they simply stood, unaware that their lungs were expanding, and drank into those unsuspecting bodies this thing called air, and then made that air breathe. And perhaps in that first breath they saw possibility …

Imagine the bold courage it took to stride forward into the very making of this place, to make its stories and then make *us*. Imagine that first breath as it was breathed via them, into this earth, to be given on and into us.

Mankujba

One extraordinary time, I felt the strangeness of an unfamiliar terrain, akin to what those Mermaids surely felt through their soles as they first walked on the land. A strange new pressure of wet pebbles and the tickle of moist sand pushing itself between toes that until then had walked only in dry, dusty earth. As I pushed my feet into that new gritty dampness, the sensation grew upwards and soaked my body in its rough, but velvety, texture. The rubbing of those grains of sand made dry, almost-humming noises that were strange in my ears. I hear that uneasy teeming still, and how its noise became grinding reverberations, discordant with the rhythm of my goodalu and of my kujiga.

I was a child and I'd travelled a long way from my home. I was visiting the ocean. They said:

go walk on the beach,
go swim in the ocean

and the sand I found there was such a foreign thing. It wasn't anything like the hot dust and gravel of my place. I'd felt something like it occasionally in the aftermath of floods, when wild water rushed to carry trees over boulders, and the carcasses of animals got caught in barbed wire. When the job of water became a cleansing of Country, when dust became mud that rotted buried gum leaves and hid the gravel, just for a moment, until tiny green leaves sprouted new everywhere.

But ocean sand was different. Where was the bindi-eye that was always worrying my feet? The sand on that beach created a million minuscule pressure points under my soles. It tried to swallow my feet and the salt water rushed to carry off small shells and seaweed that caught in my toes. For me, then, sand and shells and seaweed remained just what they were. I struggled to listen or think or feel or see or believe their indecipherable story. There was no story talking to my bones, into my soul.

Sand lies somewhere between the coarseness of gravel and the ephemeral nature of dust. I read little touches of joy and sorrow and thankfulness there when I looked well enough. Our story is like the sand ... in between, in places where joy has bothered the sorrow to let gratitude through. And it turns out that much more than sand lies in those quiet spaces where the shadows lie and cling, in those secret places between coarseness and an ephemeral maybe.

At home now, the sharp edges of the gravel biting into my feet remind me to tread wisely and the dust between those hard edges softens and gentles the way into new stories. On that long-ago day, standing on the edge of the ocean, I struggled to take that salty air inside my body and though during the course of my life I have built a friendship with the ocean sand, it is the gravel and dust that are home for me. And, like the becoming of good friendships, I crave that gravel and dust comfort, away from that other place, the place of sand, that makes odd noises in my ears.

Here, now, at my place, sitting in the shade of this rocky outcrop, I feel Garranjini, and rise to stand and walk through these grandmother paperbarks, with their generous girths softened by layers of coverings. My feet sink into the composting, not-yet-earth, leaf litter, formed from the dropped foliage of the paperbarks, leaves that have fallen for aeons, making a place for insects, and spiders with inverted funnel-shaped webs and caravans of ants, all trekking on their various journeys. The air here is so fresh that it bubbles into my lungs, bringing the complex scent of the bark-stained water and perhaps something of those ants and spiders too, but the air is mostly clean, waiting for my memory to live in it. And I see inside my body to the blood travelling through it, bubbling with the energy living here in this place from all of those lives who have been here before me.

And then the wind arrives – the great feigning thing, seeming to just drift in a casual dance along an unmapped route. But watch how it makes the grass twist and turn. Can you see it? Snapping a stalk here and discarding a leaf to move it over there, sneaking into spaces and places and claiming the voice of others to tell its story.

A curious thing about this wind, and about reminiscence: they travel together, holding memories, making gifts of the vast pure past. As the wind runs, its fingers pick up something here and a little something else there. It plays with our ears and with our bare skin, lifting hairs and brushing against us. It holds those whispered but vivid hints of place and space and occasionally it drops a clue, a memory, and we remember. Live with Country in mankujba, so you don't miss the stories as they come to you through your feet and goodalu and kujiga, or through the wind's ticklings. Through the scents that recall older times as we get ready for times to come.

* * *

The wind runs harder now and the clouds scud overhead, building up slowly from those first wisps. Now they are looking a little like the soft feathers left on the turkey after we've plucked the big, protective outer ones from its body.

That soft under-feather, hidden, until we burn it from the turkey as we roll its corpse on the coals of the fire. As we burn, the wind is there, picking up the scent of charred feathers and skin, burning with fat oozing through flame and flesh. The intermingled smells of feather and flesh and fire float free to re-form with life newly given around us, on that wind.

Those three Water-women travelled and journeyed over other lands and they held ceremonies to make stories. As they went, the wind lost more of the ocean salt, as it brushed through trees and grasses and played with clouds. For the women, feelings of closeness with their home were becoming fainter, fading in familiarity, as they journeyed inland. The water, drying from their skin, dried from their thoughts but they continued and made the country as they travelled, keeping busy making the place we now know.

When they arrived at what has become Gudanji Country, they were tired and mourning such a long separation from the salt water, long left behind. I imagine them, after travelling through the rough, dry country, maybe bringing some of that dry with them, getting down to the business of creating that mighty Garranjini escarpment. And so it sits there now, hard and dry, towering over the water that lies at its feet, reminding us of the ceremonies those women celebrated throughout what is now termed the Northern Territory. And when that rock imagines itself so big and rough, the water reminds it of the softness that created it by embracing the escarpment as it rushes through the mouth of the rock. The Water-women missed the ocean and there at Garranjini they held the big ceremonies, big business, and called to that water.

So, it came to them, that water, and it flowed over the rocky escarpment, taking a mouth-shaped gap from that harsh rigid surface. Perhaps the water missed the women too and was just as eager to be reunited. It washed and ate away the rock. As those women started to feel better at that place, they got to the business of creating the greater Gudanji community. We, Gudanji, were born of Garranjini through the freshwater and hill country – ngurruwani Gudanji-marndi maga guda gurijba iligirra gamamjani.

Today Gudanji go to Garranjini, time and time again, and see where the water ate away the rock and left there its mouth memory, and we talk to the women because they are still in that place listening, watching and making. We let our feet take us through the sand, walking a certain way, along a path forged long ago. We notice the newly exposed pebbles and our feet sink into the sand. We return because the water that flowed over that rock, washing its way to Garranjini, flows within our skin too, and the water washes away all that we collect from other places and reminds us that water always reshapes to its skin.

Memory comes with us, guiding our path, as the soles of our feet touch that earth. We walk with the gentleness privileged by deep knowing of our welcome because, like a

mother welcoming her child, Garranjini will be waiting and
allow us to again make our mark on her skin, into our heart.

always take care when you place your feet
in this earth, and in this water

the old people have lived here, they have died here too
and it is their bones that make the dust that blows across
the plains
and their story that you breathe into your body

they watch, at your shoulder as you travel to other places
and sometimes their whisper plays its way into your ears

someone has walked this way before and as you walk
yourself
into their footprints, their story becomes yours.

Under the skin

But something awful happens here, and it sits in this country and is waiting. And we walk with the story of those awful things – sitting just under our skin and inside the skin of our Country.

If you look carefully, it's possible to see the pain as it lies in the landscape. Can you hear the wail in the wind and see the blood running with the dust? There is danger, too, in the stories that have come out of the bodies of our ancestors and are sitting there, waiting for us to look and to hear them, and they cut with sharp edges honed by the awful things done in this country.

Sometimes, in some places, the story seeps out and, like the sap of the bloodwood, hardens and falls to the ground, dry and crumbling, taking that story back into the earth. All of us know that terrible things happened here, and one day I hope we might be able to be smart and speak through that pain that curls into itself and keeps the words away, to let the words free and start to heal the pain.

Listen well when this country is telling you our story. Listen with your feet in the sand and your heart in your hands and give it over to this country. She deserves it most.

* * *

As a child I sat with my two sisters and our mum and dad at the fire, watching the gidgea logs burn to coals that could cook a nice, charred edge on a goanna. This night, though, it would be chunks of the recently killed bullock charring on gidgea. The gidgea burned and its dry heat worked its way under our skin and smoothed the dryness already there from the sun, becoming an extra layer of warmth. There was often a chill in the air at night in this place. We sat in company with our old stories, living our new stories and speaking our place into them where they came together. Our dad didn't often waste air with words; he practised a silence that let other stories be told, so as we sat with the gidgea, we learned to hear and feel those stories waiting in the gaps between the noise.

The sparks rose into the air and danced there – in celebration of a whole lot of things, I imagined. The deep hot red glow in those little hearts with their flaring skirts of blackened edges held my eyes. The embers twirled above our heads, in a dance on a sigh of wind barely there, and as

I gazed upwards into the darkening sky, the just-appearing stars spotlighted larger ashy flakes. The bright burning cinders, exuberant and light, then faded to tiny pieces of black falling char. I smeared some of the ember dust onto my arm and gazed at my skin with its ash-filled pores. The light was going fast now but I had that memory.

We were waiting for the coals to be right before Mum and Dad tossed on the beef. Our share from the recently butchered bullock, the killer, was always rib bones and skirt, and a range of offal including milk-gut and sweetbread. Occasionally we'd have short ribs, but they were really popular and so shared around. Mum was always given some of the most preferred cuts because she had small children and old bush people cared about those things. We all sat and watched the fire being coaxed towards coals. Mum was feeding it sticks of the smaller dry branches we'd collected earlier that day and, every so often, she'd rake over the coals. The pile of beef sat on a small wooden cutting board, and she chased the flies that were still hanging around and cut the beef into smaller pieces with Bimbo's knife.

My sisters and I sat, gazing into the blue and yellow flames. It was almost an act of worship, tending the fire. My next youngest sister couldn't control herself and she reached for a small twig and tossed it on the fire from where she was sitting. Mum looked at her but continued preparing the meat, shooing the flies with little flicks of the knife. Secured by the hard, hand-carved gidgea handle,

Bimbo's knife continued to slice through the flesh in sure, neat cuts.

Bimbo and I had made that knife together. That day, he'd carefully beaten it until its iron blade had found its way out of the heated metal. He'd carefully heated and folded and hammered the metal that was now a fine, sharp blade. I'd worked to provide the heat and my arms had turned the steel handle of the bellows so many times that the heat of the coals had transferred into my shoulders, and I felt the burn of worn muscle. Over and over, he'd heated and folded and hammered what, days before, had been a length of iron dropped from a passing truck, lying discarded by the dirt road. My arms had become as hot as the forming iron, and I'm sure he stopped because I complained so much of the fire-pain in my arms.

Jolly, my sister, reached for another stick and tossed it into the fire and immediately reached for a third when there was still no reaction from Mum. She walked her backside towards the edge of the swag we were sitting on and sat quietly again, drawing lines in the dirt. Soon the stick sailed into the flames, and another was picked from the pile.

'Don't even think it,' Mum said, without moving her eyes or hand from fly watch.

Jolly had burned half of her hair off once when we were in our caravan. She'd been twirling around, showing off her long, freshly washed and brushed hair. It wasn't until she had little flames and whispering smoke around her ears that she'd realised her hair had accidentally flicked into the gas fire that was boiling water for tea. Jolly had started running in panic and so Mum ran after her. Jolly knew it wasn't the usual game of chasey but didn't seem to be able to calm the fright in her feet. She ran harder. Mum chased and switched between attempting to toss a towel over her daughter's lit head to flicking the towel at it to extinguish the climbing flames. Soon, the fire and smoke were both gone but now little black twisted worms fell from where Jolly's fresh and clean hair had been. Those worms and their awful smell lived with us in the caravan for so long — an ever-present reminder to her to walk and not run and to keep her hair to herself. She paid much more attention to those black worms and their awful smell than she did to Mum.

Jolly settled back and reclined on the swag, her stick now twirling in the air above, writing notes we couldn't read into the sky. Jolly was left-handed and whenever we were in town and back in school, the teachers would try to make her use her right hand. I expect they were worried it was the devil's work to be using the left. I know that because we attended Sunday school and heard a lot about the devil and about right and wrong and guilt and sin. I would see my sister crying in her class and tell Mum, who would visit the school shortly after to explain to the teachers that Jolly was to use her left hand or her foot if she chose. Jolly would be left to learn again in peace until the next time, until the next new teacher came to Camooweal with ideas from the latest books and old long-embedded religious beliefs from another place, convinced it would all make us better.

In her own childhood, our mother had sat for scholarship tests at Camooweal State School in Queensland in 1961. She was almost thirteen years old. On the morning of the tests, one of her friend's dogs had come to school — from the compound, she said. At Camooweal, the compound was where darker skinned Aboriginal people lived in a range of vessels deemed fit for occupation, not necessarily human. One was an upside-down cube-shaped metal water tank with squares and rectangles cut into it to form doors and windows. At that time, the compound had one centrally located tap for fresh water. The authorities had decided living in a heavy metal box, in a place where temperatures were often in the forties, was better than living on country.

There was a rule saying no dogs at school, so the local policeman, who had come to school that day to support the principal, shot the dog out in the playground in the middle of all the children doing what children have always done in the mornings before class starts. He then walked up and down the aisle of the classroom wearing his gun in full view as the students did their exams. Mum said he wanted to make sure that everyone understood cheating would not be tolerated.

From her efforts that day, Mum scored 100 per cent for both English and mathematics. She always considered that she'd 'failed' the third subject, geography, with a score of 85 per cent. She said it was hard to draw good maps with nib pens because the ink made things messy. She always worried at the pea-sized callus on her middle finger, which, she said, gathered ink stains that could spread and smear their way across the paper.

She'd prepared for those exams with the guidance of Mr Matheson. Mum and her teacher were both dedicated to the serious business of learning, but Mr Matheson had peppered the learning with moments of joy and benign trickery. One of her favourite recollections was when he would ask her to collect the toffee that his wife regularly made for the class. Mr Matheson always told Mum to whistle when she walked back across the school oval bringing the hard, sticky toffee. She said it was only many years later that she realised why she'd had to whistle and why Mr Matheson always chuckled as she walked back into class. It is impossible to chew sticky toffee when you're whistling.

Ian Matheson became the director-general of education in Queensland. Much later, when I was a remedial resource teacher, I presented a seminar to show how a colleague and I were responding to high-level learning needs in our Mount Isa schools. Mum's old scholarship teacher was there. He thanked me for my work, which he called new and ground-breaking. He then said that I reminded him of someone and asked where I was from. When I told him Camooweal, he laughed and said, 'Of course you are. So how are you related to Maxine?'

In spite of the very good overall scholarship results achieved by my mum and her fellow students, several years later a 'modified curriculum' was introduced at Camooweal State School. Soft and spongy, with immature and irrelevant content, it was a response to the concern that maybe Aboriginal students were not capable of learning as others could. It was the students who were assumed to be in deficit, and no one asked about teacher ability, knowledge or training. Mum said it was disappointing and enrolled me as a student at the Brisbane Correspondence School as soon as she could. There I studied the same curriculum as non-Aboriginal students supervised by Mum.

Mum was a teacher with a deep curiosity about everything, not just what was contained in the curriculum, and she was pragmatic about teaching and learning. She was prepared to battle with the devil if it meant Jolly could use the hand that made sense and she certainly taught us more than 'Suzy sea-snake says s, s, s, and Momma moo-cow says m, m, m'. Mum told us what sea-snakes were, where they lived and what they did there, and that momma moo-cow may have been black and white or tan and white because those cows were raised for milk and not beef like the cows we were familiar with. At school, we had spent hours singing about Suzy sea-snake, often as we stood to attention behind our desks in the heat of the old tin classroom.

Jolly couldn't pretend to lose her books with Mum; nor could she pretend to have a sore hand. Other teachers had the devil's work to keep Jolly interested in school. Our nanna often said that something must be tickling Jolly's blood and perhaps it was. Jolly often laughed and just did stuff that was more mischief than the kind of behaviour expected of us who had grown up in that era. Jolly was definitely not the 'be seen and not heard' kind. Maybe Nanna was right because Jolly shared the tickling in her blood, always bringing laughter. When she saw a particular old man at Camooweal, Nanna always said, 'Idle hands breed idle minds and idle minds breed mischief', but I knew Nanna was talking about a mischief different from my sister's.

As we sat there by the fire, the stick continued to make notes in the sky, but Jolly wasn't looking at what she was writing. Instead, she watched as Mum went to fill the billy from the waterbag on the car, and then slowly rolled towards the fire and, as she lay there, placed the tip of the stick into the flames. I looked on as the tip flared into gold and Jolly quickly gave it a little flick, leaving a glowing coal on the end of her writing stick. As she lay there, she brought it closer to her face and gently blew on it to make it glow hotter.

'You'll burn yourself,' I warned, breaking the quiet we all sat in.

'Will not,' she responded.

I tried a different type of reason. 'Well, you gonna goomboo, Jolly. And it's gonna be cold tonight.'

She gave me a long, considered look and said, 'That's not even true.'

'Nanna said! And I don't want to be cold,' I told her.

When Dad was out in the stock camp we all slept in one big swag, the five of us, and Nanna always said that if you played with fire at night, you would wet the bed. It was one of the little sayings Nanna would slide into a well-timed moment of conversation, like her favourite old and worn bone-handled knife cutting through one of her freshly baked loaves. She had many sayings that we all lived by – idleness, in particular, was frowned on in my family. Jolly gave me another look, this one filled with frustration and disappointment, then quickly drew some patterns into the air before tossing the stick into the fire with disgust. Apparently, she didn't want to be wet tonight either.

Mum returned and the billy was pushed into the fire. The coals had built up a fair bit now and Mum pushed them around with another stick. My youngest sister, Bligh, who'd been mostly quiet, became restless and so I played with her and cuddled her.

'Thank you, Bub. I'll give her a feed when I get this cooking. You can watch this beef for me?'

'Mmm, okay.' I snuggled with my youngest sister and tickled her belly to make her laugh. I thought Bligh was the most beautiful thing I'd ever seen. She smelled fresh and reminded me of that moment after the first big Tableland rain when the breeze blows away the final bits of dry weather. It was the smell of country with the wet grass and the aroma of older life washed clean, and new life coming. Her golden skin was soft and her hair was thick, black and curly. She was perfect. She was old enough to be walking and becoming more independent, but she wasn't doing much of either; nor was she making much attempt to talk.

Mum worried that Bligh should be trying to talk more than she was, worried there was something wrong, but Nanna said she was fine. She would say, 'Well, why would she talk or walk? There's no reason for her to do anything. You're spoiling her. Let her get hungry or thirsty, then she'll talk.'

Bligh was never hungry or thirsty and we could never resist carrying her with us. Looking back, I think it was difficult for Mum and Dad to let any of the three of us go without. By the time they'd had us, our parents had already been traumatised by the possibility that someone's misdirected and unnecessary concern could get us removed. Nanna and Bimbo, our maternal great-grandparents, were the only people they allowed me to spend time with, away from them. No one else was trusted enough.

Jolly had given up trying to play with the fire and was now lying on her back, making frames against the sky with her fingers, and Bligh was chewing on a book while pulling Jolly's hair. I picked up one of my books and started to read to them both. I was constantly trying out the new book words, enjoying the way they grew in my mouth and then their birth into the air. When I was younger, I'd imagined those words sometimes floating free to dance with other words, seeping into the air where I couldn't see, drifting to hold hands and growing until they could make other stories.

It was like when I'd imagined that Slim Dusty was a collection of music and words, not a real person, and I thought those words and music lived inside my dad's wireless. I imagined that when Dad turned it on, the words were freed and they travelled with their music companion, enabling us to hear those songs. I imagined them arranged in some other space, for us to sing, wherever we then travelled, free and out into big space. Then, one day, in Camooweal, Slim and Joy, as they had subsequently told my eight-year-old self to call them, parked beside the town hall where the library was also located, tucked away at the back. I was there looking for new books to read. They invited me to sit and have a cool drink and they asked my advice on the best books in the library, and I realised my thinking had not been totally right but was also absolutely correct. Slim was a real person, but his words did travel with us and we could sing them aloud to warm the air that then wrapped around us as we journeyed.

Mum always kept books in our swag – her books and some for the three of us. There were no books for Dad. He had no use for them because he didn't read words on paper. He heard them in the voices in the wind, whispering through the grasses; he saw them sitting in the hills and living in the rocky outcrops and he felt them as he rode horses across all that big space. Dad's words were thick and deep and came with pieces of other lives and times, like those book words I was learning. His story-knowledge lived inside him and travelled in country, coming from the old people, through and on, to us. He read stories in a landscape that was full of them.

Dad never complained about the sharp corners of the books that lay under the blankets with us at night. He knew that we had our Gudanji story through him, and he understood there was another story taking over our place. That story, living in those books, with their strange words holding onto paper pages, which I was always curious about, was something necessary for us to learn. Dad said we had to learn those stories that lived in books and travelled in other ways because our country had changed now, and we had to find a way to live with it.

Dad arrived back at our camp, a little away from the rest of the stock camp. There were a few gidgea trees that formed a bit of a screen and he had parked the car so the stockmen, or ringers, at the main camp couldn't see us. Dad always kept us away. He kept us safe in the most basic way possible — separate from others — and placed where he could see everyone who might be coming to our camp, coming near us. Trauma had made newer stories inside my dad, and he was still learning how to live with them as they pushed and jostled the old stories. Sometimes the newer stories became too big for Dad to keep them inside and they pushed their way out with a violence that mostly Mum but sometimes I, too, had to deal with.

Dad washed his face and arms in the small, enamelled basin with its soap scum floating now in reddish-brown, frothy clumps. The basin was chipped and battered. One of the horses had even stood on it one day, but it held water still and was a better washbasin now. The horse's hoof had made a little rise in the middle of the bowl and created a perfect place to keep the soap out of the water. We'd put fresh water in it that morning, but Mum had already made Jolly and me wash, and we'd spent the day roaming the dry creek bed and climbing trees looking for the budgerigars nesting in the hollows. The yellow bar of Sunlight soap with its smears of red dust and snappy gum bark sat on its little throne in the middle of a red-brown puddle now that Dad had washed. He'd been riding all day and always ended work covered in fine red bulldust. The whole day dust had been thick in the air, mingling with the smell of milling cattle, of manure being trampled into the ground and drying in the heat. And when I'd sniffed carefully in the middle of the day, I'd also caught, on just the right thread of air, the burning odour of flesh from the branding irons. It had all settled now.

The harshness in the smell of burning flesh was different. It was still there but it seemed softer now that the sharing of a meal was in progress. We were all silently acknowledging the life sacrificed by the bullock to enable us to live — the process from branding iron to plate. Everywhere in the stock camp, with the coming of the setting sun, most things had found an order.

All the water had been carted in; there were dry creek beds around where we camped but water only ran there in the Wet and now was the Dry. We were always frugal with water, being careful to take only our share.

Just before the sun had started to sink, I'd watched as the last of the budgerigars came back to their hollow-log nesting hides. There were so many that they cast shadows over the ground as they flew. The huge flocks flashed and reflected the sun as they wheeled and twisted together, turning the empty blue sky a beautiful sap green and then emerald. In that moment the heat of the sky would disappear as it was flooded with the green traffic of hundreds of birds. Their shrieks floated down to settle, with the dust, into the earth, bringing a softness that was often missed in that black soil country. I thought their shrieks were as lovely as the music of Tchaikovsky that the new teacher at Camooweal school would sometimes play when I was there. I watched carefully to see where those birds closest to us landed and where they entered their hollows. If I looked properly, I could find them the next day and check if there were any eggs in those nests. And, if I was lucky, I'd find babies with the green tinge of future feathers shadowing their grey wrinkled skin. Those babies would sit with their huge eyes and big beaks gaping, waiting for parents to return to feed them.

There was a silence now that wrapped around the landscape, getting everything ready for sleep. Cattle occasionally stamped and bellowed, and there was the sporadic metallic moan of the old windmill, several kilometres away, but these noises didn't sit in this country; they sat on top. We listened carefully and, through the strange new noises that didn't have a story here, we heard the quietness of the old stories drawing nearer. Night was coming and it was time to sit with that silence and move closer to the fire.

Threads of gidgea scent now caught in the smells that still swirled through the quickly going light, and the fire glowed against the rising blackness. The sun sent out a last morsel of itself to illuminate the night ahead, then its light was gone, and the coolness of air untainted with dust and cattle smells and bird noise rolled over us all. The warmth of this fresh fire radiated new and welcoming heat.

The meat hit the hot coals and its sizzle sent out a fresh

cluster of smells and tiny puffs of white ash. We watched as the fat from the ribs rendered and then ran into the coals, making miniature flames explode around the beef.

Dad came and sat on the towel Mum always made him sit on. She didn't like a dusty swag so once we were on it, after we were clean, we weren't allowed to move. It was the same for Dad. Mum often had us up early, so she could fold the tarp over the bedding, protecting it from the dust of the day. There were no shelters or tents out there because who would want them when we could have the stars?

Mum came and sat on the swag, tickled Jolly and sat Bligh in front of her to feed her. I moved a little closer to the fire and turned a thinner rib bone and raked some more coals flat.

'Show me that stick, Bub,' Dad said, and I passed him the long strong twig I was using. He'd made a long cooking fork for Mum with some heavy-gauge fencing wire, but the stick played with the ash and coals better. He turned some more of the coals, then put the skirt and milk-gut on the carefully prepared bed, and we all took a collective breath at the sputter that rose when the wet dribble of milk-gut touched the fire.

The smells of charring bullock flesh rose around us and Dad told us how he and his mother used to cook this same way. My Gudanji grandmother liked rib bones, and julkabudi. I did too — we all liked eating goanna.

Our mouths pulled into smiles as we all sat and gazed

into that fire to travel to another time or to perhaps bring our paternal grandmother to sit at the fire with us. I preferred the julkabudi tail, but the adults mostly ate that. I enjoyed stripping the pale meat from the leg bone just as much.

'How did she like eating her rib bones, Dad?' Jolly asked.

Dad laughed and told us she liked eating rib bones with the fat dribbling down her chin. We all laughed some more, imagining the deliciousness of our gidgea-cooked meat, with the flavour of those coals and the fat running down our chins too. In fact, Mum was always wiping our faces, so the fat didn't get to drip too often and I hoped perhaps this time she'd be a little slow to insist that I clean my face.

Through the laughing, the fractured pictures in my head came together and slowly merged. I drew in a deep and slow breath and lifted my head to imagine my grandmother sitting there with us. Dad would often tell me I took after her, that I walked just like her, that I was tall, like her ... but mostly, he always said, I was cheeky, just like her, and that always made me glad.

I deliberately slowed my gaze as I looked for my grandmother sitting on the other side of the fire. I found her. She turned her head to me and grinned and nodded her head at the fire. I looked at the flames, then back to her, but she wasn't there anymore. In that glimpse to the fire, she was gone but I knew she'd been there because my heart felt sore and lonely, until I felt the fat dribbling down my chin and remembered that I was cheeky like her and maybe she hadn't gone so very far after all.

Dad picked the bits of milk-gut and skirt off the coals and gave them each a sharp tap against the smooth rock that sat beside the fire. The last fragments of coal and ash fell away from the meat to leave little dips of char that we knew would be flavoured with gidgea. Each piece was added to a plate and I blew on the small pieces Dad gave to Jolly, cooling them.

We ate our dinner and grinned at each other when the fat from the rib bones dribbled down our chins and Mum made us wipe it away. Dad brought the laughter back when he said that on his day off we would go and get a goanna. I didn't see my grandmother at that fire again, but I felt her close and I knew that, just as we'd eaten gidgea into our bodies, our grandmother had brought her presence into our stories. She would be with us when fat dribbled down our chins and she would run with us to chase the goanna we planned to get, giving her strength to our legs to ensure we caught that swiftly moving julkabudi.

After we finished eating, Mum lined us up for another face and hand wash in the beaten enamel bowl before she played a game of tiddlywinks with us, and Dad strummed Slim Dusty songs on his guitar. We all sang for a time in soft voices because it was night, the time for sitting quiet and still.

Dad waited for the flames to burn out completely and when the coals lay in a soft glow, draped with ash, he put some more gidgea on the fire and it started a gentle smoulder. It would slowly burn all night without flame now, and Mum would be able to quickly start a fire to boil the billy in the morning.

Jolly and Bligh were soon asleep, and I tried to read some more words from my book but there wasn't enough moonlight and the fire had burned down too much for any light. I thought the darkness that had made it impossible to read my book might be a message from my grandmother, telling me it was time for our stories, not those words from books that didn't live with the soft fires and cooling breezes. I went to sleep under the stars with my family and our stories all close.

An ending

I thought I knew what pain was, but then my mum died. I felt the unanaesthetised and raw slashing of the cord that day. And it was only at that moment that all the pain I imagined I knew, and had known, became real. The cracking of multiple bones, including three in my spine and two ribs, while breaking in my horse, the cutting out of tonsils, the numerous moments of slashed flesh during childhood accidents and the birthing of my ten-and-a-half-pound son all lived in that moment and coalesced into a soul-deep tearing wound defined by, but unable to be contained in, my mother's passing. I felt that my life was truly my own in that moment and I wasn't ready, and I didn't want it and I understood the horror of a single separate story that focused on me.

Isn't it a curious thing to stand in a crowd and to feel blood and pain spilling everywhere and, in that moment, you are utterly alone, the only one who can see or feel it running rampant in your body? I think we must all live it in that moment of our mother's death — the separateness and isolation intersected by pain. Perhaps that's the rite of passage: the separation that has apparently happened at our birth but that we live again when our mother makes a final physical departure. It's a strange kind of knowing that makes sense of the gifting of life then, in that moment of death — the becoming with others.

A mother's life blood nurtures, and the bloodsucking infant feeds. As she died, I thought perhaps she was taking back all she had given me. She wasn't, of course. This woman had endured torture for me. The nerves threading from her body to mine had now been truly severed as she exhaled her last breath. The well-used, stained and ancient blade of death tore away the arrogance in which I'd wrapped myself and exposed things in me I'd never thought were there. I faced knowing that she was nowhere I could conveniently reach her, talk to her, in my time, when I wanted. And across the gaping hole of her grave, an old memory came to me in a tune, long forgotten until my mind turned from that vacuous hole to let memory wander. A tune I once took great pleasure in singing to my mum, during my rebellious teen years, came back to me. It was a Billy Joel song, telling someone to 'go ahead with your own life, leave me alone', but of course my version was filtered by teenage angst, so I sang, 'go ahead with your own life, leave me to mine'.

I'd assumed I was prepared because the looming end to her life was documented by hospital visits to treat the cancer that had taken over her body. I had sat in the palliative ward and told myself she was looking well. My inner ostrich didn't read 'palliative' and had drawn calm from her rounded face, telling me she was gaining healthy weight rather than that her kidneys were failing. Angry and appalled at myself, looking at my family, my sisters and our children and our dad, arrayed around her grave, I was ashamed to know and own my false strength. I offered a silent and long-overdue apology to Mum and promised to kill the darling ostrich. And it came to me that she had birthed me; her blood, her flesh and her bones were mine. Maybe Mum had not gone too far away and maybe I could find her if I found the right way to seek.

And when, into the hungry, gaping mouth of earth, her coffin slipped, I struggled to draw breath, as if her now-still lungs were seeking space in my body, and I fought for my breath. The dust motes rose from the hole that was swallowing her and I sucked them into my body – a final shared breath, my mum and me. I drew in the dust motes and the breath of the earthly mouth and buried them both deep inside, to absorb them into the marrow of my soul, trying to entomb the dust that entombed my mum. And as still I watched, I recalled more words from my dark and moody teenage years. It was a Dylan Thomas poem, urging the dying to rage, but my mum was not the kind of woman to rage … except for that one time. So, she is gone, my mother is gone, and in this earthly separation her bones and her blood and flesh now become truly mine to do with what I will. Oh, the obligation!

Protection

I was told they came to get me after I was born. Despite being a healthy baby of good birth weight, I had not-so-good skin colour. I was darker skinned than my mum but fairer skinned than my dad. About twenty-one years earlier, my dad was born on the banks of the birthing creek on Wakaja Country. That place, our Country, which we have never ceded, had been taken in a moment by others and renamed Alexandria Station, which is in the now-named Northern Territory. In that claiming, we had become a strange entity on the landscape, a moving entity not quite human and a little beyond animals, perhaps. By then, the Australian government had implemented various iterations of the Aboriginal Protection Act, legislation which claimed to take care of Aboriginal peoples but was really concerned with trying to hide the obscene acts of colonialism, and there was much to be hidden. There was a chief protector who ensured the laws were enacted. It was a collection of the most abhorrent rules controlling the 'dying race' and 'smoothing the pillow', apparently for our own good. So, Dad was born 'under the act'.

Despite the act being created to protect Aboriginal people, he suffered terrible trauma at the hands of white pastoralists, too many of whom were armed with guns and false claims that were often used to justify unspeakable deeds. So, one day, Dad left, needing little encouragement to abandon the country that had been his family home for more generations than we, or science, can count. He had been accused of poddy dodging – stealing the young unbranded calves. It was only the most recent accusation levelled at him. I've often wondered how they thought he'd done that. As a young teen, he had extremely limited English and even more limited opportunity – he had no one to sell the calves to. The Protection Act didn't afford him any protection at all. The act, if a person wants to take the time to view it, is a carefully worded document enabling the vile behaviour of lawless and evil men and had little to do with helping Aboriginal people. Dad made the journey on foot and horseback from our place into Queensland, chased by white men armed and threatening death. His family, bush and story knowledge, and remarkable horsemanship, allowed him to cross the border at Camooweal, meet my mum and make a family together with her.

When I was still a child I'd heard Mum's mother call him the 'myall blackfella from the Territory' any number of times. Back then, I thought it must be okay to be called that, it must be a caring title, and so, for a time, that word became part of my identity. Then I noticed it was always spoken in fugitive ways, by people my parents were uncomfortable with, and it was never spoken in their presence. The title was and still is, of course, derogatory. It was meant to put my dad *in his place*. The myalls were those Aboriginal people who could not call themselves Spanish or Italian or Greek or Afghan. They were the people who could not read or write English well enough to apply for that awful Certificate of Exemption, which gave Aboriginal people the promise of controlling their money and mostly their lives too. With his dark skin, my dad was just a *myall*.

I, along with some other dark-skinned children, was called that name several times as I grew. A particular storekeeper at Camooweal imagined he was funny and would often call me myall and he would watch my face, like the hawk watches for injured lizards and bugs after a fire, ready to pluck up the terrified animals running from the flames. Like the hawk, that storekeeper would watch for any indication that his wicked words had pierced me. But I knew he feared the myalls because I noticed that, like Mum's mother, he never spoke that word in front of my parents.

I was considered to be that strange funny kid because

of who, what and where I was. I rarely smiled and was always preoccupied. It wasn't due to sadness that I didn't smile. I was simply too busy being curious and learning, to read words and silences. Smiling meaninglessly wasted my time, when there were other opportunities for genuine joy in celebrating a worthy occasion with a smile.

Some people said things to me like, 'Smile, your face won't crack', and sometimes, 'Why are you so sad?' I wasn't any more or less sad than the next person, but I was curious, and those comments and the time wasted in forming a response they would find palatable irked me. To take that question away, I wore an expression that encouraged neither conversation nor comment. Because I didn't fit into the fabric of where we were or who I was supposed to be, I spent an inordinate amount of time inside my head. Nevertheless, for the most part, I was happy and comfortable there in my physical environment and I was utterly safe in my mental space. There was, however, a deep inquisitiveness within me. I was never the kid who asked, 'Are we there yet?' I was the kid who asked, 'What's up that road? What's around the next corner? What will happen if ...?'

Dad had returned from the station's stock camp, where he worked, and it was pay day. He took me into the store to buy something. The storekeeper came out from the back room to serve us. He smiled his smile that always made me feel my skin was slimy and dirty. You know those smiles

— the teeth all exposed under the blank, soulless eyes. My dad knew I didn't like the storekeeper but I'd developed a curiosity about his attitude. Whenever I was nearby, I watched. I noticed the way he interacted with people going into and leaving the store and I watched his face and I listened to his words. And I disliked him more.

I'd never spoken about this curiosity that grew from my dislike. I'd never told Dad of my dislike, but Dad knew the important stuff without being told, and so we entered the store with his hand on my shoulder. The storekeeper asked what we were after, and I hated his smile and his watching eyes that made me want to scratch off my skin. With my dad's hand rubbing my back, almost urging me on and giving me his strength, when the storekeeper said my actual name, I asked, 'Why didn't you call me myall today?' It was fascinating to watch the teeth disappear and the eyes come alive with panic.

'What was that? What are you talking about? I'd never call anyone that. You must have misunderstood.'

And, just like that, the dust motes stilled, and an anxious silence pervaded the store. Those refocusing eyes saw me, and I saw that there was something else now reflected in them. I'd never assume it was respect, and he'd never mattered enough for me to want that, but I saw that, now, he saw me. We still didn't like each other but, in that moment, we at least saw who each other really was. I learned that day that if you stand up to bullies, they often run.

Belonging

So, in those early days, they came to get me. Someone, I can't remember who, told me that I was also 'under the act' because my dad was and that he and I were aliens in Queensland, illegals. I was also told that several times it had been Mum's mother who had alerted the authorities to our whereabouts, so *they* knew how to find us. And there was a time that my dad was threatened with jail because of my birth. Mum was incredibly young, you see. In her family, when I was little, I remember a lot of tension. It wasn't personal, it was never about me, just that she had given birth to a child and my dad was a myall. My dad provided for Mum and me, just as he was expected to. He did it because there was love between Mum and Dad, but the police, who acted in place of the 'protector', were sent messages about our family when we were in town, and then *they* came.

Mum's grandmother, my nanna, always supported both Mum and Dad, but Mum's mother – not so much. If she had reported us, maybe she did so out of fear; I certainly don't know. It's an unspoken thing that's ignored by those in Mum's family who know. They claim ignorance and being shocked, but it's always sitting in the corner of hearts and conversations, and it gnaws into relationships, changing their shape. My growing was done with a distancing between me and my maternal grandmother because I was a child of that time, and though I was seen and never heard, I absolutely saw. I could never be comfortable with her treatment of my parents. I eventually made my peace with Mum's mother by accepting I had no way of knowing her story well enough to understand her behaviour, and we eventually developed a good and easy relationship, but it didn't happen until I had reached adulthood and had my own children. Then I could find a way to accept we all have our failings, and I have plenty too.

In those days, Mum's family lived in a tightly knit and isolated little community where people worked hard and kept out of other people's business. They worked hard to merge into the community and perhaps that was their protection. And we went to Sunday school at the Methodist church and observed the Catholics as unobtrusively as they observed us. After the Sunday services of fire and brimstone in straight-backed pews, and when collection plates had been fed, the men retired to have a quiet drink and the ladies did whatever it was that ladies did on the rest day. I think perhaps the Country Women's Association cooked scones sometimes for after church and though the women in my family then were never invited to join the local CWA, before I was born my mum was part of the choir of Aboriginal girls, 'little half-caste lasses', who sang for the ladies who ate those scones.

Mum's family had a tough life, and mostly it was like everyone else's life, but they cultivated a level of mediocrity that gave them some invisibility and protected them from the harsher reality experienced by darker skinned Aboriginal people. Still, I think it was a fragile protection. And it was too hard for me to exist in that identity twilight. I struggled to find a place of equilibrium, where I understood who I was. My dad solved all those issues for me. On the day, when I was about seven or eight years old, I noticed absolutely that Aboriginal people were treated differently from others, I asked Dad why it was so. He answered simply that people were like that now. He said we were black, and I should just get on with the things that mattered, so I did.

Several times when we travelled into Camooweal to visit Mum's family, my sister and I had to sit on the back steps of our grandmother's house. When we were little, she didn't always invite us inside and the back steps were always in full sun. Frequently, the soaring temperatures made it seem that we sat inside a shiny glass heat box with burning light jumping all around us off the galvanised iron walls. One day, the heat enclosed us, taking moisture from our mouths to leave only that pasty stickiness that makes it hard to swallow and causes your tongue to swell. My sister started choking on her dry mouth, so our grandmother came out through her back door with a small, enamel cup containing water. I gave it to Jolly and she drank the half-cup of water that cowered in the bottom and then I wiped the drips with my fingers, sucking up the moisture before it could evaporate in the heat.

Mum's family are Aboriginal and, in the 1960s, with their fairer skin, they never identified as Spanish or Italian or Greek or Afghan as many others were doing to ensure some protection for their families, but neither did they identify as Wakaja. They just were, and maybe Camooweal made it impossible for them to be Wakaja, but it was hard for me to find myself there. I couldn't read myself into belonging because I didn't know the stories; I couldn't find them anywhere because even the silence was empty. I always felt there was something else, that something big was missing. Mum's sisters were beautiful and loving aunts and Mum's aunties were wonderful, tough, nurturing women, but I struggled to find the niches where I could see or feel who I was and where I came from. I was rarely comfortable, always on edge and defensive. In my head, I was watchful, and it still hurts that I felt that way because there was no need. Back then, the only times the voids and gaps were filled was when I was with my dad. It was easy then. Easy in ways that were beyond the strained interracial relationships of the 1960s and 1970s in remote outback Queensland and the Northern Territory, but absolutely a result of them.

With my dad, I had a history, I had a connection, and it was straightforward. It was hard and it was difficult in many ways, but I found a space that I could fit into, that was my shape. I was Wakaja because my dad had gone through Wakaja ceremony and I was Gudanji because my dad had Gudanji blood, and I was as entangled in our place as the vines of the Gudanji wild cucumber bush, ngamarragama, or the jimbalurry, the Wakaja mistletoe. All across the country that Mum and Dad worked, and where we lived, was my place, my home. As I walked on Country, I walked in the same places my ancestors had walked for thousands of years. The brutality and horror in the treatment of Aboriginal people became something else – a flaw in the character of others. As with the storekeeper, I felt sorry for such a soul-deep flaw, and I did not allow that to make me into a victim. Because I was proud of the tough, quiet strength of my ancestors, I became mindful of my behaviour and how it might affect them or reflect on their legacy. I watched more closely and listened more deeply and took care of how I walked on Country, always enveloped in the ancestors' strength.

Meeting

We met during the term break of the final semester of my teacher education study – saw each other and decided we needed to be together, that we would marry. Nearly as quickly as that, and though he took three 'dates' across a week to ask the question, the asking was almost an exercise in convention because there was no doubt about what my answer would be. Our eyes connected across a smoke-filled room and we didn't feel any of the clichéd cynicism in that, just an immense relief that it had happened, that we were both there in that wonderful moment together. It was the 1980s; we were at a disco, and all the cool kids smoked. We didn't, but neither of us has ever worried about being cool. Since then, I've forever thought our meeting was always going to be and I am glad I didn't have to wait longer than the twenty-one years I already had.

We knew we would struggle with the same hardships and worries that all people do as they start building a partnership, but we were convinced that those who said it wouldn't last were wrong and we were stubbornly determined to prove it. We agreed on a verbal prenup – no credit card, no divorce and no violence. We've achieved two but fell at a hurdle about two years into our marriage and got a credit card. Before debit cards came along, it seemed to be a thing when checking into accommodation while travelling, and we've done a lot of that.

He was a surfer from the Gold Coast, and I was from Camooweal – kind of. I couldn't tell one end of a surfboard from the other and was sure that water was only for drinking – to sustain life – whereas he'd been raised in this other kind of that wet stuff, salty and undrinkable. He was barely able to tell one end of a horse from the other and I was three when my dad put me on a racehorse he was to ride. Dad told me to look at how far it was to the ground so make sure I held on tight and didn't fall. From the time I was seven, I helped Dad break in my own horses. He was a whitefella – a marndaji – and I was a black woman – a ngarrinja.

I took him home to meet my parents. I told him how important it was that he didn't say anything about our plans to marry just yet. We'd known each other for two weeks by that stage and my dad would have hit things, lots of things, if he knew we'd already planned to marry, and Mum would have had a crying jag. There were too many complications and we needed time to fix things, to make him part of the family first, so dinner seemed a good first step.

When I was growing up I saw a movie, a classic that starred Sidney Poitier and was called *Guess Who's Coming to Dinner*. It was about a white woman introducing her black partner to her family. The 2005 remake of that movie plays with the storyline and has a black woman introducing her white partner to her family, and the scene where they have dinner with her parents is almost, word for word, what dinner was like at our home that night. Bernie Mac made a good job of playing my father.

My dad spent dinner sending long silent looks across the dinner table that caused the roast beef to cool faster than the pumped-up portable air conditioner watching from the corner of the dining room. My future husband struggled to be comfortable, but the poor man developed a nervous twitch, and I truly don't know how he didn't realise that stabbing the fruit in the bowl in the middle of the table wasn't the best way to become part of the family. Neither could he read the silences. Rick tried to fill the gaps with conversation, and my parents and I sat in confusion at his lack of contemplation. At the end of the night, my toes were sore, and though Rick's ankle was fine after several days, I was worried at the number of times I'd had to kick it to signal to him to nod and not shake his head or vice versa. Staying focused on the conversation and kicking Rick at the right time to make him respond appropriately took much of the pleasure out of eating Mum's roast.

Later, when he had left and my parents and I were reflecting on our first experience of hosting a stranger to dinner, I was asked to explain why Rick had spent the entire night stabbing the fruit. Mum lamented the cost of the fruit and that the apples were already yellowing, and the bananas were ruined. She wondered why his mother had not taught him how to be a good guest. My dad asked if Rick was a wasteful person since he had destroyed the fruit so casually with his sustained stabbing. I told my dad that he, himself, had caused the problem: if he had been more talkative, then the fruit would have survived because Rick would have been occupied with conversation. But I wasn't sure if that was the solution or perhaps even another issue altogether.

Mum's worry was mostly surface – she'd been charmed that Rick had arrived at the door with flowers for her – but Dad wasn't impressed with the roses and at the end of the night as we sat, he asked, 'You know he's a marndaji, Bub?' and just to be sure, repeated it, but this time in English, 'You know he's a whitefella, Bub?'

Rick was and is a dream I hadn't imagined possible and, unlike Conrad in his *Heart of Darkness*, claiming 'we live as we dream – alone', my plan was not to dream alone. I come from a culture that has never existed in the story of individuals. I intended that our lives would continue joyfully with no darkness in our hearts. So, I looked at my dad, grinned and pretended shock: 'Oh no, is he?' I laughed and Dad's mouth crinkled to the side of his face, in an attempt to hold in his grin before he turned away, scratching and shaking his head.

* * *

Dad is with Mum now. I stood with my sister and our children, and we tossed in gum leaves and then we shovelled in the dirt. They'd spent all their adult lives together and now they were in the one grave as they'd wanted it to be. They were both disappointed that, because of Mum's early death, they didn't make fifty years of marriage. I remember the times we discussed death and burial. Dad would make silly jokes and laugh, wondering aloud who would go first and who'd be 'on top'. Mum would pretend not to get the innuendo, but her eyes always sparkled. They had a relationship that was starkly honest and many times deeply brutal, but I could always see the love, flawed but continuous.

I don't know how to talk about my dad no longer being here. It is too big. Mum and Dad both gone is still not a thought that I can hold inside my body or my heart, though I'm comforted that they are together. Throughout the privilege of a full childhood with my parents and my two sisters, with the joys and sorrows and, yes, the violence too, there was always love – imperfect and damaged, but always love.

Gidgea and bones

I saw fish falling from the sky in rain showers at Camooweal. I suppose it must happen in other places. Tiny fish would wriggle on the grass and gather in the little puddles of water on the ground. The water would mix with dust and would turn milky and pale like the sweet cloudy water in the river. All the kids would run around and collect up the miniature perch that were frantically trying to stay in the running streams of rainwater flowing back to the Georgina River. Many people don't believe it, but it does happen — this curious thing of fish falling from the sky and, like the fish, my memory wriggles and twists to find the life threads that take me home when the water falls from my eyes.

When I see a chestnut horse or a Bedford truck or sometimes it's the sails of a Southern Cross windmill, water falls from my eyes. When I hear a Slim Dusty song, eat rib bones or sit by a gidgea-fed fire, I cry because it's too big, but I do those things on purpose, with purpose, to remember and be with my dad. And I recall the stories Dad told us of when he was a kid, walking for months to the Gulf for salt with the Wakaja mob. I know that, like those Water-women, the salt in my tears brings my dad back to me.

* * *

He stood outside the pub in Mount Isa waiting to meet the Oban Station manager who, word had it, was looking for a bore mechanic. It was going to be a change of scenery, but he thought it was worth having a go. The work on Rocklands, located not so far from Camooweal, had come to an end. The seasonal work was good to fall back on but there was always more work to be found to get through the off-season and so he would take up a stint of bore work to tide the family over.

As he stood there, Dad turned his back to the road and pulled his hat lower on his head. The hat was marked with sweat stains around the brim coloured with the dirt of many Rocklands musters. He tilted it to the angle he did when he was mustering paddocks in the late afternoon. When the sun shone at a particular angle, the low-tilted hat kept the heat from his face and stopped some of the dust, some of the time. At mid-morning, this particular day's hat tilting was to shield his face. He'd never been one to stand around outside, or inside, a pub. He struggled with the shame of it. He had a deep and bitter loathing for all alcohol and had shunned it all his life. He looked up and down the street but couldn't see anyone who might be a station manager. He'd been standing there a bit now and had even tipped his head to acknowledge several men he'd worked with in the past.

'Hey, Soda, what you doing here? Coming in for a drink?' one of the younger men asked with a grin.

'Ha, nuh, nothing doing there, mate,' was the inevitable reply.

As he began to consider that the message about work may have been a false lead, a man came out of the double doors of the pub. The stranger stood on the rough rock paving, lifted his hat and scratched his head. Dad noticed one hand had no fingers, just a palm with a thumb, and wondered what might have caused that. Likely it was a bore accident. The stranger looked up and down the street, scanning for something or someone. Dad did the same.

Nothing much to be seen on the street. The usual old man staggered along the footpath looking for bumpers, those half-smoked, discarded partial cigarettes carefully sought by those without the money to purchase a tin or packet of tobacco, and the same collection of people went about their usual business. A few delivery trucks rumbled by and the station utes were all covered in various shades of dust that gave hints about where they'd travelled from.

Up the road was a parked Land Rover, which Dad eyed for an extra moment or two. He wondered if it might be from the Territory, with its dressing of red dust. He missed the Territory but wasn't about to risk his family by returning there. Behind the caked mud, he saw that the number plate said it was a Queensland vehicle.

'G'day mate,' the stranger said, tipping his head by way of an older type of greeting.

'How ya going?' Dad replied.

'Not too good right now. I'm supposed to meet a bloke to take him out to the station, but he isn't in there. I don't have the time to wait for him. I gotta get back this afternoon. There's a bore run to do.'

'I'm waiting for a bloke too. Was s'posed to meet him here an hour ago. Maybe had a job for me.'

'What kind of work you after? I don't suppose you know anything about windmills. I'm looking for a bore man. What's your name anyway, mate?' And the stranger, his hand extended, peered at Dad from under his broad-brimmed hat.

'Well, happens I know bores. Name's Soda.'

Dad was a skilled mechanic. We restored several Bedford trucks together, including putting in the electrics and building the engine. He would often create the parts he couldn't source or purchase easily. He would pick up random pieces of wire or metal as we drove along isolated roads and fashion them into the parts he needed. The early cardboard cornflake boxes made very nice gaskets for the Bedford.

As a youth, before he went to Queensland, he worked with a Scottish engineer called Ted McFarlane. Mr McFarlane taught Dad about the workings of the engines that were needed on cattle stations and Dad's innate skill and curiosity extended that knowledge. When Mum and Dad moved us into Mount Isa, where my sisters and I attended high school, Dad worked as a plant operator with the Mount Isa City Council and had a reputation for being able to operate anything and everything. He had learned and honed his ability using his knowledge methods, working through Gudanji ways of knowing and without ever having the privilege of western schooling.

I'm told the stranger laughed as he grasped Dad's hand and shook it. 'Well, good to meet you, Soda. I'm Henry, Henry Corbett from Oban Station. We were supposed to meet. I was looking for you in there.' He gestured to the door of the pub.

'Well, you gonna have a long wait in there. I don't drink. Never have, never will.'

The man laughed again. 'Good to know, Soda. Come over to the Land Rover and we can have a talk about the job, or do you want to go and find a cup of tea? Do you drink tea?'

Dad was a serious tea drinker. Drank his tea from a great big quart-pot pannikin that was stained black from the strong brew he made in it and from which he'd then drink. His tea was so important that, like many of the old bush people, he didn't let anyone wash away the tannin that clung and layered itself to the inside of his cup. On the day when the horse he'd been riding stepped into a hole, and rolled and broke its leg as well as Dad's, it was the quart-pot surviving the fall that Dad was most grateful for.

Dad and Mr Corbett talked, and they were each satisfied with the other, so Dad went to Oban Station to work. Within weeks, arrangements were made for us to also travel to Oban. We were to live there. Mr Corbett said there was a house. Dad was proud, Mum was excited, and I was suspiciously curious.

Windows

Dad's old job at Rocklands had come with a house. Well, it had come with a roof and four walls built of the standard corrugated iron and locally cut posts and was put together enough to be called a house. It was the typical building of the day. No more, no less. They mostly had dirt floors but then, according to who would live there, sometimes the dirt was covered in flat rocks, which allowed you to hose water to lay the dust. Sometimes there were wood floors and, sometimes, a layer of vinyl made a real difference to the amount of dust that invariably rose through the spaces in any floorboards.

That Rocklands house had an inside sink. The metal sink was a smaller version of a cattle trough – the same as was used to water the horses in the stable yards – and there were two taps. The tap hanging over the sink was brass with a latched top; the one outside, also brass, had a turn top. The sink stand leaned to one side, a result of white ants eating away at the leg in the corner. There was a partition in the house that only went halfway to the roof, but that broke the inside space into two separate areas. A living area and a sleeping area. And there were windows.

The rough squares cut though the corrugated iron were framed with skinned lancewood and gave an air of something else to the building. Windows made it a house. They could be opened when you wanted them to be open, by propping them with a stick of lancewood. All around the inside of the house lancewood sticks were propped against the walls beside each window, waiting for moments when the outside was allowed to come in.

Some window props were a bit fancier, with notches carved at intervals along their length to allow the windows to be opened to various gaps. I had seen some in town that were pieces of neatly cut timber and not tree parts at all or, rather, parts of a tree that had had its memory trimmed so much it had forgotten its roots. Window props were sacred, and everyone knew not to touch them because, if they were accidentally tossed into the woodpile, there would be some woman bringing trouble.

But we hadn't lived in that house. We'd lived on the outside, in the caravan, on the other side of the fence – with the livestock. All stations had a fence that protected the living areas from the random wanderings of the cattle. The people lived inside the fence but some people lived with

the stock outside of it too. I'd looked at that house inside
the fence so often and wondered what it would be like to
live in it, because it was a symbol of something that was
apparently unattainable for us. Every so often, my sister
and I stood, holding the fence wire in between the barbs,
just gazing at that house.

As I was there one day, a slight breeze lifted my hair
and tangled it in the barbed wire. I interpreted the tug of
pain as I pulled my hair from the wire twist as a reminder
that I shouldn't be gazing over the fence, but I refused to
feel that I was invading. I could see the heat dancing from
the roof and if I walked further along and looked from a
different angle, I saw the silver glare of the sun bouncing
off the tin. I imagined it was some kind of presence telling
me to mind my own business, to stop looking.

Flies took advantage of our preoccupation and gathered
around our eyes as they always do in the bush. We blew air
through pursed lips, from a slight opening at the side of our
mouths, to try to make them leave. We were interested in
the house, the flies in the moisture traps of our eyes and our
mouths, if we opened them. I could feel them on my back,
gathering on my shirt, in the shade, resting from the heat
of the sun. I hated flies so I swiped at them to chase them
off my face and then carefully wiped my hand across my
sister's face to remove them. She blinked and we continued
looking, barely registering the flies.

That house stood on its little block of dirt over past the

store, and the butcher shop, and in the opposite direction to the manager's house and the mechanic's shed, all inside the fence. A couple of jackaroos, the sons of other station managers, lived in there now. Station managers always sent their sons to other stations, where they'd be taught, schooled in the same lessons and values they all lived by. These boys walked around with stock whips and attitudes that it was best to keep away from. I always thought them a strangely arrogant bunch. They learned the trade from the experienced Aboriginal stockmen, the ringers, but soon assumed they had the knowledge and the right to direct those same men, the first source of all their jackaroo knowledge.

They could often be heard discussing how their families had been on their properties for three and sometimes four generations and they wore that history with real pride. They never bothered to imagine how it might feel being on country for thousands of generations. Their claims were made according to the monuments that had been erected on that land and had totally ignored and brushed aside the hospitality offered by country. Or perhaps the hospitality was invisible, just as the stories told in other voices were too quiet.

The jackaroos were frequently sunburned and would have blisters on their hands and often be saddlesore. They dressed in the uniform of moleskins and blue collared, button-up shirts, sleeves rolled to the elbow, and they wore flat-heeled riding boots. A few times, one would come to the station wearing a pair of spurs. I always heard the ringers laughing at that. And sometimes there were white men among the ringers who shared a friendship free of colour-induced boundaries and they too laughed. The jackaroos' hats were as flat as their boots and most of them had two. One hat for work and one for wearing to supper, but which was left on a long stool at the door of the dining hall, when their boots were polished and cleaned of the earth and the cattle dung. Maybe they even had two pairs of boots, I don't know. Sometimes the jackaroos would be polite and make conversation but often they would spit at exactly the place where my feet were, without giving any indication that they'd noticed I was there. They were teenage boys working out how to be men in places where the lessons were covered in red dust, sweat and a social hierarchy based on skin colour, historical untruths and a true empty silence.

Back then, when my sister and I watched through the fence, I'd occasionally push my foot through and touch my pointed toe to the other side. Quickly, I'd pull my foot back. Mostly nothing happened so I'd do it again but every so often, maybe when the house presence was watching, or maybe *because* the house presence was watching, my foot would catch on the barbed wire and my flesh would open and drip blood onto that dry earth.

And, on the other side of the fence, the drops of my

blood would fall and splash into the soil. Little puffs of dust would dance up from the ground. Through the barbed wire I'd let my blood run into the dust and sit there. My blood blended into the red dust and it put me in a space where they said I couldn't be. As it dried, the thin layer of mudded blood would lift around the edges and smooth into the centre – a minuscule curl of me and earth – on the other side, while I watched, it faded and crumbled back into the dirt. It may even have blown throughout the enclosed homestead area on the dust, taking me with it.

Often, I would trace a line in the red dirt and leave my mark there but when it looked a little like a snake track – and I never wanted to call out the snakes – I would carefully add more marks. The snakes were often poisonous where we lived. Perhaps the julkabudi would come, I often thought as I made more marks to show a brushing tail with trailing claws beside it. A goanna would not be a bad thing.

Mum always came out of the caravan, which was parked a little way off towards the creek, and shouted that we were to get back inside, that I had schoolwork that needed doing. We would leave the fence with only my goanna marks showing we had been there, sometimes accompanied by a drop or two of blood. It was okay that the blood took me there and I thought that if it wasn't about me maybe the blood was telling us the julkabudi was soon to be with us.

Our dad was a stockman, but we lived outside the fence, some distance away from the house. One day, I turned and looked again through the fence and, as I watched, one of the jackaroos turned on the tap that lolled against the corrugated-iron wall. Water rushed out and he splashed it against his face and brushed it off his hair. He shoved his hat back in place and off he went, towards the supper shed where the cook was hitting the iron bar, sending out a ringing sound across the fenced-in space, calling them to eat.

Just then, Mum called to me, 'Get your buckets, Bub. We'll get some water before Dad's back. Watch Bligh for me, Joll. Leave her in her bed, but just watch her, okay?'

I walked back to the door of the caravan and picked up the two smaller buckets that were stacked by the metal pull-out steps. Mum followed and picked up the other two larger buckets and we made our way, not towards the tap, but through the dolomite rocks and boulders to the creek. I watched the black soil and looked closely at the holes that hid under the edges of the rocks. Some weren't holes, just strange, shaped shadows of the rocks, but some were large, gaping mouths in the dirt. Snakes lurked there and I always hoped I'd drawn in the legs of the goanna quickly enough. We went to the flat rock that was half in the water and I stood back while Mum went to the creek's edge and dipped her bucket into the milky stream.

An almost-breeze came across the water with the scent of the ever-present pink waterlilies and damp, but the heat of the day was still enough to burn the soles of my feet, so I danced, quickstepping from one foot to the other before either could burn. The milky water blended into the surrounding beige, and I often thought that it hid itself in plain view. It was the same washed-out paleness that pervaded the landscape as far as you could see, as if it were too hard to distinguish different colours from one other. The steady step from one foot to the next got faster the longer I stood there, soles burning now, and I started to hop instead. Mum passed the filled bucket back to me and I passed her the next one. When her buckets were sitting flat and balanced, I topped up the spilt water. When she had taken as much water as we could carry in our buckets, we slipped our way off the rock and onto the dirt. Our wet feet left muddy prints as we slowly made our way back to the van. I played a game with myself, trying to step into the foot marks left during our journey to the water. Mum's prints were too far apart but mine were exactly right and, as I turned to look at the strange footprints following us back to the van, water splashed and dribbled down my legs. The toes at either end of my footprints were fooling my eyes, hiding the direction of my journey, making the mundane task of collecting our water from the creek into a mysterious adventure.

Mum rescued my buckets and used one to add water to the half-filled, battered enamel mixing bowl whose job it was to remind us to wash our hands. Soap scum floated on the top from the Sunlight bar that had been used that morning. The remaining buckets of water were placed in the shade by the caravan. Mum and I mostly made the trip to the creek in the morning and in the afternoon, but today was wash day, so we did an extra trip for water to wash the clothes waiting in the wicker basket. Dad would be back for supper soon.

Mum and Dad often tried living apart. We would occasionally live in town and Dad would live out bush on the station, but none of us were really comfortable with that. I think, too, that Mum felt better protected being with Dad. The threat of having children removed had mostly gone by that stage, but I imagine people who have lived through such things don't ever regain faith that they or their children are safe. So, we often moved from town to station and back again.

Sometimes, Dad worked on the road gang that established and maintained the roads from Camooweal to Gregory and Burketown in the Gulf of Carpentaria. One time we were out there, my sister Jolly had a fit and both our parents were terrified she would die. All the other workers had gone into town for the weekend and we were alone at the remote camp. Mum and Dad didn't have a car then, so Dad hotwired a work truck to drive her into Camooweal to the hospital. Halfway along the road, Jolly came out of the fit, sat up and started telling Dad to look at the moo-moos. Mum decided she was probably not going to die after all, so Dad turned the truck around and returned to camp. He meticulously parked in the tracks the truck had previously made and then we all had to dust away the evidence of our trip, using small branches from the gum trees to brush out the tyre tracks and our footprints.

While we lived in the road camp, school went on. My books would be completed and then sent back to Brisbane. At our camp at Red Bank, they were kept in two pine fruit boxes that slotted into each other, carefully but surely protecting my books. When it was school time, Mum carried the combined box into the shade of a tall gum. One of the fruit boxes was placed on its side and the other was stood on its end. They morphed into a desk and seat and so I worked at the learning that was outlined for the day. Mum would go about her work, cooking, washing, and taking care of my sisters, but she always came and sat with me and read.

She also checked my work and always insisted on it being repeated if it was not correct. She and Dad both believed that having to repeat anything was a waste of time that was too hard to come by, so I grew with the practice of doing it right the first time. But my motivation was different from theirs. I just wanted to get the schoolwork over with so I could read or go somewhere to listen to the stories being told by the wind. They both worked hard to ensure we were fed and clothed – neither of them understood the contemporary need for 'me time'. Mum said to me once, 'What is the point of having children if you need to have a break from them? Raise your children to be people you want to spend time with. Do that, or don't have them at all. If your children are such that you need a break, look at yourself and your mistakes and fix them quickly.'

Sheltering

Mum and Dad were able to borrow money from a forward-thinking storekeeper in Camooweal who, without any records or paper trail, lent them what they needed to buy the van. It was a 32-foot Viscount with blue stripes along the sides. That caravan made it possible for us all to have a bed, somewhere to sit to do our schoolwork, and Mum didn't have to cook on an open fire if she didn't want to. We were flash and though it wasn't the stockmen's house, it was much nicer, much more than the tin shelters that other Aboriginal people were then typically expected to live in while working on stations out that way.

The van also caused problems, of course. At that stage it wasn't entirely legal for my parents to own such an asset; it was against the laws of the Bjelke-Petersen government, so they didn't advertise it was theirs and many people assumed it wasn't. Mum and Dad always kept a roof over our heads and food in our bellies, and they did it any way they could, within the bounds of common decency.

After working at Oban for a few weeks, Dad came back across the long and dusty beef roads, through Barkly Station, to Camooweal to pick us up and take us back with him. He and Mum had spoken about the move and Mum had us organised and ready. The plan was that the EH Holden station wagon, recently acquired in a trade for his EH Holden ute, and Dad's staple way of getting around after a horse, would have the caravan hitched to it and off we would go. Mum would pack a lunch of sandwiches, a flask of tea and frozen bottles of water that would melt as we travelled. We wouldn't have to stop.

I was a little worried about leaving Camooweal – Oban seemed so far away – but I was also relieved at the same time. I'd seen two of the town's grannies fight the previous week and it had frightened me a little. They had stood in front of each other and held their fighting sticks in a way to make the traditional starting taps. I have a gudbajirra now that I am an adult, a proper fighting stick made a long time ago before my birth, of the fire-hardened gidgea that all good Wakaja women should have, and I expect that if we ran forensic tests, there would be an interesting array of ancient DNA embedded in its time-roughened surface.

Back then, the grannies almost danced as they took turns hitting each other on and around the tops of their arms. Their movements were guided by rules decided long ago, for how to correctly fight with a stick – no one moved out of the way of a hit, certainly neither dodged, and each took their turn in the right order. They were both honourable, law-abiding women and fought as Wakaja and Gudanji women had always fought, holding their sticks the right way. I think it was assumed that if you were ignorant enough to not know how to hold the stick, then you deserved the inevitable smashed fingers. The heavy hitting continued and, each time an arm was hit, exposed breasts would shudder with the shock waves travelling from the stick through the body. I'd sat with the other kids and watched and with every hit the echo travelled through the ground and rattled my bones. The grannies fought on for such a long time that it was surely only the momentum of their measured back-and-forth stepping rhythm that enabled them to remain standing. I don't know why they had to fight but I know there was trouble over someone taking a perentie when the law said it should have been someone else's goanna. With the move to Oban, I looked forward to having some space to think about fighting with sticks and following the law.

We got into the car and, with our caravan trailing behind us, left Camooweal – Dad driving, Mum nursing our little sister and Jolly and me sitting in the back seat. When we'd had the ute, with its bench seat, my place was the hat rack that ran behind the seat and if I bent my knees just so, I could fit comfortably, kind of, lying along behind the heads of Mum and Dad, so the station wagon, with an entire seat for Jolly and me, was luxury.

The wind brought dust in with it but it was the Dry and the road wasn't too bad. The caravan happily kicked up dust into frothing red feathers that followed us for a bit, then settled back onto the road. Long stalks of tall yellow grass formed a guard of honour as we travelled across the plains. We played games of spot the turkey and several times tried desperately to convince Dad to stop for the goannas that would run across the road and then lie still and flat in the shelter of the yellow grass and amber shadows, but we needed to get there so he didn't stop. Besides, Mum said she refused to turn up at the new station with a dead goanna in the car.

Then, after we'd been driving for a bit, the car started to slow. 'What's wrong, Dad?' I asked, putting aside the book I was reading aloud. I noticed both Mum and Dad were watching the far horizon in the direction of Barkly Downs Station, and my gasp was heard in the car before he could answer. I saw a smoke plume in the distance.

'You got towels, mate?' he asked Mum and quickly parked on the side of the road.

Dad jumped out of the car, told us to get out as well and ran around the caravan checking that the windows were still secured and hadn't been shaken open by the rough road trip, but he opened its door. He came back, took Bligh and Jolly and put them in the caravan. They were both crying now so Mum went with them.

'Soda, what will we do? That fire is coming this way fast,' Mum said.

'That's not a fire,' he answered. 'Get inside and shut the door. Me and Bub will be back soon.' He turned to me. 'Give me a hand here, Bub,' he said, and I ran behind him to the car.

As I looked again towards the horizon, that plume of smoke was growing even larger into the sky and swirling into great billowing clouds. The clouds seemed to dance, and I thought they looked like the flocks of budgerigars and the way they fly at Wanarda, in the Territory, but the black colour was all wrong. I hadn't seen smoke dance like that before and couldn't understand what kind of fire it was, but I understood Dad was worried and that wasn't a good sign. We were in the middle of a wide grassy plain and the grass was almost as high as me. It had been a decent wet season, all the old people had said, and now, the good grass that had grown had already dried out nicely for the cattle. Too bad we were a long way from the last of the good water that was lingering in the creeks now because, though it was strange, it still looked like smoke to me and that meant fire.

Dad gave me a towel and told me to plug the air vents in the car. He had the bonnet open and was doing something with the radiator and engine. He then told me to wind up the windows. I did that and, as Dad grabbed the keys from the ignition, he pulled me across the seat and slammed the last car door shut. He dragged me along behind him and I noticed grasshoppers jumping across the road. As he bundled me into the caravan, the light started to change, bringing with it a strange, blurred hum.

I ran to the closest window and looked out to see more grasshoppers flying towards us – they were everywhere outside. I'd never seen so many grasshoppers before. It only seemed to confirm that the fire was bad: the grasshoppers were on the move, so why were we staying still? Mum and Dad were talking quietly to Bligh and Jolly because they were still upset and then there was a strange crunching noise. At the window I could see nothing through the thick covering of grasshoppers. They crawled on the fly screen, and some were chewing it. The light was nearly all gone now, and the darkness made the noise seem louder. And then an ugly sound made by thousands of hungry grasshoppers hitting the caravan grew and caused us all to look around. I wondered aloud if they could possibly eat through the walls of the van and asked Dad if they could. He assured me they could not, that we were safe.

In our caravan we sat in the dark and so, to keep us thinking of things other than the horror of grasshoppers and strange fires, Dad told us stories about the headless ringer who rode around on moonless nights at No. 3 Bore on Alexandria Station. When Mum growled at him for scaring us, he told us we were safe, really; we were too far from Alexandria. Besides, the ringer was headless and therefore without eyes, so he couldn't find his way anywhere. Mum rolled her eyes at him and fanned us all to keep some of the air moving. Sweat ran down our faces and it was hard to breathe in the sweltering heat, but the noise was still there, and it was still yellow-dark outside. Mum took a bottle of water from her bag and we had a drink. Dad stood up and pulled three grasshoppers from the wind-up air vent in the roof of the caravan where they had squeezed their way in. Jolly screamed. He took a bowl from the cupboard, turned it over and captured the trio underneath.

Dad took a cigarette paper from his pocket and licked the pointer fingers of both his hands and started talking. 'Look here now, I'll show you a trick.'

He stuck a little torn piece of white cigarette paper to each fingernail. 'Watch the paper. I'll make it go away and come back without touching it.'

He bent his arms, moving his hands up and down to his shoulders. Each time he put his fingers down on the tabletop, the paper had disappeared and, in the next turn, reappeared. It wasn't until many years later that we caught on to his trick and understood he was playing a version of Two Little Dickie Birds and merely changing his pointer fingers for his middle fingers.

I don't know how long we sat in the van. It seemed an awfully long time. When the light came back, I looked out of the window again and Dad, looking with me, said we would be able to go outside soon. When we did, the sight that met us was incredible. There were dead and broken grasshoppers everywhere. I didn't know where to put my feet. As I walked through the carpet of insect casualties, I made little crunching noises. Grasshopper guts dripped in slimy blobs from much of the caravan and ran like the lumpiest yellow custard down the windscreen of the car. What had been a wide plain of shiny yellow grass now had a track of mostly eaten and broken stalks, with bent and battered blades, running all the way through it.

After giving Mum an apologetic look, Dad used one of the towels to clean the windscreen, though it still had yellow smears on it. He drove us on towards Oban but stopped at the first little creek crossing that had water in it. We all got out and tried to wash away the smell that was now living in our clothing, and splashed the car and van as best as we could, but the grasshopper remains stayed with us for the entire journey.

We continued our trip as planned, with the bonus layer of drying yellow grasshopper guts that covered almost everything, until we came to a wide sandy creek. The road wove its way across the creek bed through sweeps of sand and around little rocky outcrops. Several parts of the track had shallow streams of water running across them and we couldn't see the other side through the trees and grasses that grew there. Mr Corbett was waiting with the Land Rover.

'We'll hitch the van up to the Land Rover and pull it

across the creek, eh Soda? She's a wide one and she's got a good belly full of sand on her. There are plenty of sharp angles that might make turning slow and we don't want the old girl to sink. She'll be right with the Land Rover pulling her through in four-wheel drive.' He pointed to the van.

'Oh no, I'll be okay. I can get across there,' claimed Dad.

He and Mr Corbett walked off to examine the road through the creek. At intervals, Dad stopped to look carefully at the road. He stood back at different places and walked off the track occasionally, somehow mapping a track in his head. Slowly, he came back to the car, lifting his hat and scratching his head at the back, as he did when deep in thought. He said to Mr Corbett that he would see him on the other side.

'What now?' asked Mum.

He tipped his head, motioning to us to leave the car. After we had all piled out, we stood on the graded ridge marking the edge of the road.

'You take the kids and walk across to the other side. I'll meet you there,' Dad told us, and so off we started, moving over the dry creek. It was blazing hot and Mum took Bligh and a water bottle, while Jolly and I held hands. I carried another water bottle. We walked from tree to tree, standing in the scanty shade made by the gums and bloodwoods. Jolly complained her feet were burning and Mr Corbett asked if us kids wanted to ride across the creek on the back of the Land Rover with his boys. Mum ignored Jolly's hopeful look at the trayback of the big four-wheel drive and quickly declined with a simple, 'No, thank you.'

In some mottled shade thrown by a sparsely leaved gum, we swapped baby for toddler, Mum hauling Jolly to her shoulders while I put Bligh onto mine. And then we walked some more. Mostly we walked in a straightish line and managed to keep pace with Dad as he slowly zigzagged his way through sand and rock. Mr Corbett, with his three sons on the tray of the Land Rover, drove and parked at various spots throughout the creek. Mum plotted a path that mostly managed to keep Dad in between us and them.

Mr Corbett would park and smile at us, calling, 'Are you all right?'

'What's that marndaji doing that for?' Mum asked no one in particular.

We all stopped and looked at a tree near the Land Rover rather than directly at him. We were careful about not looking openly at the vehicle and its occupants. We continued to walk until the bank on the other side came into view. We climbed up the eroded side through crumbling sandy soil and stood waiting for Dad.

The van, playing follow-the-leader with the station wagon, slowly made its way through the last of the creek. There were times when they travelled slowly at a steady pace and other times when Dad seemed to do side drifts through sand and lonely leftover puddles of water. Jolly laughed when the rooster tails of sand and water sprayed up because they left rather lovely patterns of red mud and stone in the air. Dad was nearly at the other side as we climbed the last washout and stood looking back across the track through the creek bed. Unfortunately, we made the mistake of standing near the road and before Mum realised the error, the Land Rover had pulled up beside us. Mr Corbett jumped out.

'Well, he's certainly making a good job of getting across there without bogging. It was tricky enough in this one,' he said, patting the Land Rover.

'My Dad is an acc–, mmm … an accomplished driver,' I stated before Mum could comment. I'd read that word in a book recently. They had said the character, a wonderful piano player, was accomplished but I had thought Dad's driving was as wonderful as any piano player, so it was a good word to apply to him.

Mr Corbett's eyes travelled from my mum to me and I didn't need much of Mum's push to move behind her and try to hide, but my curiosity meant I kept him in sight. He smiled at me and I felt my mouth wanting to give an answering smile, but I fought it and won.

'Oh, I can see your dad is an accomplished driver all right. So, what's your name then?' he asked.

This time Mum beat me. 'Her name is Debra.'

'Well, Debra, Mrs Corbett has made some patty cakes for us all for smoko. How does that sound? She made pink icing for the top of them too.' His smile beamed this time, straight at me, but again, before I could respond, Mum answered.

'Oh, we have food … but thank you.'

And with that she grabbed my hand and walked swiftly, almost dragging me, to where Dad was just parking the car. She took Bligh from my shoulders and put her and Jolly into the vehicle and then went to the back of the car and took out the tuckerbox. She hadn't lied: there were sandwiches in there but no patty cakes, no pink icing. I had wondered why Mrs Corbett would make patty cakes with pink icing when I knew that her children were boys. It seemed to me to be a strange thing. Pink icing was for girls, for special times. Mum put pink icing on my last birthday cake but nothing since then, and the shiny red tomato, chosen especially as a treat for this trip, wasn't quite as exciting.

'You need to go and sit with them,' Mum told Dad. 'They've brought tucker. You go over there and sit with them but take this sandwich. We'll stay here.' And she pushed a paper-wrapped sandwich at Dad.

In the shade cast by the caravan, I watched them sitting by the fire, waiting for the billy to boil. I was glad when Dad refused a cake, but I wasn't sure if it was because I was relieved that he wasn't going to be poisoned today or that I didn't have to be jealous of him eating a patty cake with pink icing. He came back to us and we continued to Oban.

Mr Corbett parked the Land Rover near a house. It was a bit fancy and certainly flasher than the one on the other station. It sat on a platform, above the ground. There were windows propped open with thick planks of wood and not rough-cut lancewood poles, and there was a square of green grass at its side. On the other side of the green square sat a long, low building.

'So, this is your house,' said Mr Corbett. 'I've got the fellows coming over tomorrow to put some more fly screens in for you, but you should be okay for tonight. Do you have mosquito nets?' he asked, turning to Mum.

'We have mosquito nets, and the caravan is screened ... thank you,' she answered.

Pointing to the house on the platform, he said, 'This is the sleeping area. You've got two bedrooms in there and a small washroom. The long building is your kitchen, bathroom and laundry ... outhouse behind that. Just watch the girls in the bathroom tonight because I noticed this morning that one of the legs on the tub is loose. I'll be back in the morning to tighten it up. I won't do it now 'cause you all need to settle in. The missus has left you some tea, milk and sugar, and some veggies from the garden. We have our own garden here, so you just go and get fresh veg when you want. There's also a milking cow so if the girls would like fresh milk for breakfast, send them over with a pan, but the cowboy milks at sunup.'

He grinned at Jolly and she, being Jolly, grinned back. Then he turned and walked back to the Land Rover but before climbing into the cab he turned again and said,

'Come over in a bit and get some beef. They've been out to get a killer today.'

We all stood and watched the Land Rover drive back across the station to park in a huge open shed alongside other vehicles. A quiet collection of two adults and three children, we looked at the house arrayed around us: a bathroom with a clawfoot tub, apparently, a kitchen and a laundry, all arranged inside the station perimeter fence. Here, at this place, we were separated from the cattle; we were inside the fence.

'You have to go and get the beef,' Mum said to Dad.

'I want to get the caravan unhooked and set up before dark. Bub will go over. She'll be okay.' Dad had already decided that Henry Corbett was that rarest kind of man, the kind so rare he'd only met one other. Like Dad's lifelong friend Ian McBean, a very well-known Northern Territory cattleman, Dad had decided he could implicitly trust Henry Corbett.

Sometime later, I walked over to the building I knew to be the butcher shop. They tended to be the same on all cattle stations – mostly with half wall and half fly mesh and usually squarish and squat. If there were any hanging carcasses, they were always in evidence through a fragile veil of fly mesh, modesty attempting to bring dignity to death. There was a Land Rover parked there and I could see men walking between the building and the vehicle – doing a clean-up, I thought.

'Hello, Debbie,' a voice called from inside the butcher shop.

My steps slowed and I took a careful look around without any obvious movement of my head. I counted two men and the voice inside, so that was three. I looked at each of the two, carefully trying to gauge their level of interest in what they were doing, and, in my mind, I located my dad and calculated how far away he was. I knew he would be watching while setting up the caravan and would keep me in his line of sight. I stopped a Land Rover length from the building. Mr Corbett came to the door and grinned.

'Come in and have a look at this lot. What did Mum say she wanted?'

It seemed that he was serious about what we wanted. Peering at him for several moments that surely seemed to be much longer, I lived in a blur of confused nothingness. Pink icing, fly screens inside the fence and what my mum wanted swirled in my head, crashed and collided to become like blobby grasshopper guts. My world order was changing, and I struggled to find my head, which was off somewhere, perhaps with Alice, in Wonderland. I was reading that book at the moment.

I could have told him that Mum hadn't told me anything. We were certain there would be an already-selected collection of scrap beef waiting for me, so none of us had wasted our time considering what we might *want*. I could have told him that we were all thrown off balance because there was a house, inside the fence, separate from the cattle, and *he* was worried about the wonky leg on a clawfoot bathtub. I could have told him that I was barely able to walk on the inside of the fence, that my toe, marking the dirt, was big enough. I should have told him that I needed time. Perhaps there was a book I could read that would tell me about this strange new order of things, so that I could see straight again. Or I could have told him that we really were too scared to start believing we had the right of choice, for fear it would all dance off with the heat haze and mirages. But I didn't say any of that.

I could see that all the beef had been cut up and was spread on wire mesh shelves or hanging from hooks to cool. The smell of fresh blood mixed with the salt-laden air wafting from the brining tubs at the side of the room, and the flies gathered on the mesh trying to find their way inside, perhaps to escape the outside heat, perhaps to drink in the blood and flesh. The whole of the bullock was there; nothing had been taken. I wondered how serious he was. So, remembering I was like my dad's mum, my granny, that she and I were cheeky, I told him what we wanted.

Lenny, one of the station workers, walked a little ahead of me, pushing a wheelbarrow lined with clean hessian and filled with our beef. I imagine the three of us made for a strange little procession. I walked behind the journeying gum-leaf-covered beef with Mr Corbett by my side. He said he wanted to check with Dad that the old kerosene fridge was still running okay. It tended to be rather finicky, he told me. I didn't know what finicky was but I had a dictionary and so I would find out soon enough.

Mum and Dad came out to stand and watch as we paraded across the green square of grass. Mum tried to hide it, but I could feel her horrified look.

'She certainly knows her beef,' said Mr Corbett, smiling widely at my parents. Dad just grinned. Mr Corbett introduced Mum and then Dad to Lenny. Turned out Dad had an offsider called Lenny, if he needed one.

Mum was lucky the wind didn't change at that moment because Nanna said that if we pulled strange faces and the wind changed, we would be stuck with the strange face for the rest of our lives and I didn't think Mum would like her very strange face for too long. It seemed that along the road, somewhere between Camooweal, through Barkly and across to Oban, we had entered a twilight zone and had really arrived in Wonderland. We had arrived at a place where it was possible for a black man to have a white man as an offsider, if said black man so desired, and a little black girl could select all the best cuts of beef and be given them, no questions asked. Everything had lost the balance we had previously lived by and I was looking at this place through eyes that kept everything fuzzy. Nothing was making sense and I wondered how long it would be before my world returned from the rabbit hole it seemed to have entered.

When Mr Corbett and Lenny left and the five of us were

once again on our own, Dad started to put the meat away. There was silence from Mum, but Dad remarked on each cut of beef as it was added to the fridge.

'You got the full milk-guts, eh? And look at that, they cut their rib bones big over here. Hey, mate, can we have this sweetbread and the fillet for supper tonight? That's a good bit of rump, Bub. Gee, this bloke has given you so much beef. There's even a good-sized roast and a piece of corned beef.'

Mum finally came back from the place she had been in and snapped at Dad, 'Don't mate me, Soda. I don't know what we're supposed to do with all this meat.'

'We'll have to eat it, or it will go off,' Dad said.

She turned to me. 'Why did you ask for this much, Debra?'

'Mr Corbett asked me what I wanted, so I told him.'

Mum enrolled Jolly and me again with the Brisbane Correspondence School and our books would arrive via a little plane that had a large blue capital letter 'B' on its tail. Whenever we saw it coming through the sky, Bligh and Jolly always sang, 'Big B is coming, Big B is coming.'

The Corbetts' two eldest sons were also enrolled with the school and Mum's work was not to clean the main house but to teach. She and Mrs Corbett had talked and they each got to do what they preferred. Mum taught and supervised the lessons of all four of us and Mrs Corbett cleaned the main house. Mr Corbett said the cattle had never had such reliable water with the windmills always in service, and Dad didn't often need an offsider. And, because we had a refrigerator, Mum made ice cream from condensed milk.

The only problem was the cook — she thought it wrong that the station manager's wife was cleaning, and a twenty-two-year-old *black girl* was teaching the boss's kids. The cook took exception to Mrs Corbett taking us all into the kitchen of the main house to cook biscuits and cakes, and she absolutely took exception to Mrs Corbett dancing and cuddling with my sister Bligh, singing along with Ross Wilson, 'I'm just crazy 'bout you, babe', but Mrs Corbett didn't care about that. I can only imagine what the cook thought of the three pink lace dresses Mrs Corbett bought for my sisters and me. It showed an amazing decency and kindness that continue to make a real difference to my thinking and I remain truly grateful.

She and Mum established a friendship that was extra-ordinary for those times. When the rain came and the earth was still damp, Mrs Corbett would take us on scrambles across the landscape in the very early mornings to gather mushrooms still wet with dew. She then cooked them for us in the kitchen of the main house while we all laughed at the naughtiness of eating something that seemed to grow from horse manure. She planned and took us on picnics, and when some swagmen came through Oban looking for work, she made Mum carry a box of pepper in her handbag. Mrs Corbett said it was hard for a man to do much if he was bent double sneezing. She told Mum that she really didn't like the white chenille bedcover that Jolly had ruined with spilt red nail polish, and that she was so happy that her boys were getting good schooling. Mrs Corbett hadn't had a happy school experience and told Mum she hadn't completed primary school, so she was grateful that she didn't need to worry about that. They got all us kids involved in fixing the ant bed tennis court and the adults played tennis as often as they could, with Dad and Mr Corbett taking it in turns to cook steak and watch as we all chased tennis balls and roamed the Oban countryside.

When it was Christmas time, Dad took one of the station trucks into Mount Isa to pick up the presents. Both sets of parents had ordered bikes for their children because all our school reports were so good. My average mark was 97 per cent and I had received several prize books and had one of my science questions read aloud over the radio. My drawing of a panda in a barred zoo won an art prize and my prize book collection was now up to seventeen.

The cook, naturally, was most disappointed – a sour liver, Nanna would have said. So, the lessons had been a great success, except when Jolly, who Mr Corbett had taken to calling Bindy, would go with the Corbetts for a drive around the station checking cattle and fences. Then Mum would have to sit with her to catch up. But I stayed home to finish my schoolwork because then I would go to work with Dad. He didn't need an offsider because that was my job.

Wind

Two sails of the half-complete windmill hung against each other above me like a mortally injured pelican before his last flight to that unknown place they go to die. Dad hung up there too and, in my mind, I replaced him with a picture of a fish, half in, half out of the pelican's beak. Wriggling in the empty space full of contradiction and contrariness, both wanting to escape the death-harbouring jaws while needing to stay — to not fall, to a perhaps not certain death, but serious injury.

There was no water here except for what sat a long way underground. Dry and dusty, the landscape stretched as far as I could see, and I knew it continued way beyond the dancing heat waves. And the shine of that place, from the sun glinting on the smooth-baked earth to bounce on the silver iron windmill parts, hurt my eyes when I looked too hard. The screech of iron grinding together continued to send ominous cries through the heat of the day to surround us. It was like a reminder to turn our back and lose attention at our peril in that waterless place.

I wanted desperately to move but knew I couldn't. I looked up at Dad as he moved about his work high above me. The heat had come in and was sitting in the cab of the old Bedford truck with me. In its company, beads of sweat formed at my hairline, but they dried before any of their moisture could run into my eyes. Little flakes of salty dry sweat stuck to my face like fish scales and I could feel them curl and twist on my skin as they continued to dry out. The flies had given up even trying to get any of the moisture from my eyes and had long disappeared. I looked down at my feet, both firmly on the old metal brake pedal trying to keep the truck still.

On this day it was my job to slowly reverse the truck, pulling the bore casing and rods into place. Then, with my foot on the brake, Dad would connect them one at a time, coming down the windmill to tie each to the pulley at the front of the truck. He'd shown me how slowly the truck should move, and then how to stop and hold the rope with its attachment still until he'd connected it in place. It was a boring job, but he said I wasn't allowed to let the truck move once he told me to keep it still. Sitting on his perch on top of the windmill, Dad would then attach a rod or bore casing in place and come back down the windmill frame. He would attach the next rod or casing and reclimb the metal frame to connect the next casing after I'd reversed the truck. Then, we would start all over again, but now he was hanging the sails to complete the windmill. He had connected the vanes of the windmill, which would carry water not just to the cattle but to the birds and other little animals who lived here in this heat and would appreciate its life-giving liquid.

A red meat-ant bit my big toe. I looked down and flicked it off with my other foot, watching the huge mandibles now nudging a lost crumb from my earlier slice of damper. My toe developed a tingle and soon it began to itch. I tried to rub it with my other foot, but it didn't help. I tried to transfer my attention to something else. I thought, if I ignored the pain, maybe it would go to visit somewhere else, not my toe. I wished I had thought to bring my book. I was in the middle of Anna Sewell's *Black Beauty* and enjoying the familiarity of the horses in the story. It made me feel safe after the crazy upturned world of Lewis Carroll's Alice.

I hadn't been able to read anything the previous night because we were out of carbide. I was kind of happy about this because Dad told us about a friend of a friend of a friend who had sucked the tip of the carbide light to clear a blockage. It exploded and he'd ended up without his brain. I was responsible for the two carbide lamps we owned. I had to clean them, but Mum had shown me how to use a fine piece of straw, which I would break from the broom, to carefully clean the tip of any build-up. I needed my brain because I had two Christine Pullein-Thompson books waiting to be read after *Black Beauty*; I wasn't sucking anything. I was always fascinated at how the carbide would produce gas that travelled up the stem to the head of the lamp, which would then be lit by a carefully placed match. Mum always sprinkled the water in the chunks of carbide before pushing the cover into place and into its water pot. Then I'd watch for any bubbles, which showed if any of the gas was escaping. Dad would take the lamp outside to place a match to the tip. There was a story, of course, about someone ending up with a hole in their roof when a carbide lamp exploded and sent the blocked tip through the roof like a bullet.

I counted the cattle as they milled about us. They were thin and 'tucked up', as Dad said, which was when livestock hadn't had enough to drink and were looking dehydrated. Some came to the truck and sniffed at the waterbag Dad had hung under the tray in the shadows. Some stamped around the dry trough, but only dust came to meet their hopeful, seeking mouths. No breeze travelled at this place; it was in the desert, the dry bore. I looked out over the rocks and boulders that lay there in the heat – a handful of randomly tossed dice. These, though, had bullock carcasses keeping them company and not little black spots to represent the numbers.

My toe itched some more, and the miserable, desperate cattle lost my attention, just as they'd lost their drinking water. I looked at Dad again, trying to judge how much longer I would need to remain still. Zebra finches darted around in the shiny haze of midday. They always seemed to have so much energy. Or perhaps they could smell the water that waited below the earth, ready to rush up the casing and eventually into the trough. The itch continued.

I moved my other foot slowly, slowly. I imagined Dad could see if I moved it too quickly. Slowly, slowly, I moved my foot again and tried to brace myself enough to move forward on the seat of the truck. Just a little further and I'd be able to balance myself enough to scratch the itch. I reached down to my foot, my arm going under the steering wheel and past the door handle. My backside slid forward on the cracked leather seat and my foot jerked to the edge of the brake pedal. The truck lurched headfirst towards the windmill before I managed to press the brake pedal flat again. Thankfully, the truck hadn't stalled.

'Hey! What are you doing there?' came the yell I was waiting for. Thank goodness he was up there because I would have copped it otherwise. 'Debra, hold the truck still!'

'Yeah. Okay ... sorry. My foot slipped — a meat-ant bit me.' My voice ended in a muddle that echoed softly in the footwell of the Bedford. I was 'Debra', not 'Bub', and that meant he was annoyed or angry or both, so I gave up the idea of scratching my toe. If he decided to, Dad would climb down from the platform and then I'd have more than an itchy toe to worry about. He finished attaching the vanes of the windmill and I knew we'd be back the next day to put up the sails.

Right now, it looked like the large segmented circle it was, standing high on the tip of its little stage. He climbed down from the platform and came across to me in the truck. Opening the door, he moved gears and pedals to turn the truck off and he knew, absolutely, it wasn't going to move. He motioned for my foot and took it in his hands and turned it this way and that. When he saw the red welt left by the ant bite, he took some spit from his mouth and rubbed it on my toe.

'There' he said, looking me in the eye, our noses almost touching as we both bent over my foot. 'It'll be okay now. Didn't I tell you to keep the truck still? You let the truck move, everything moves. Rope breaks and then everything flying all which way. Tomorrow, when we do these sails, you can't let it move. You got to be the boss and watch that wind. If that wind comes and pulls the sails to make them swing around, they'll hit me on the head. Remember, I told you that story about that old man? He got hit when the wind blew up and the sails hit him and maybe it chopped off his head. I don't know all that story, but he was finished, just like that. He didn't have anyone holding that rope steady.'

'Yes, I remember that story, Dad.' I also remembered the story of the headless ringer at No. 3 on Alexandria and the friend of the friend of the friend, and I couldn't bear for my father to leave us to be headless with any of them.

'Mmm, okay. Come on then, move over. Let's get them mamugujama we saw back there before the turkeys beat us. Maybe we'll get some for Mum and the kids. What do you think?'

And so Dad and I went out across the black soil country after the conkerberries so favoured by us all, including the turkeys.

Hill country

That time with Dad has long gone now but I remember the joy of racing the turkeys to get the best of the mamugujama, and I've taught each of my three children like my dad taught me. Now, my own kids, including nephews and nieces, all jumped from the troopie as it rolled to a stop and they hit the ground running, off to the thick mamugujama shrubs that grew all around this place.

I grew on Wakaja lands, but my kids grew on Gudanji Country. And here now, with the red soil making the squat green bushes seem brighter and sharper, the mamugujama were so big they were the size of my little fingernail. They coloured the green bushes a coffee shade of brown. It had been a good while since I'd seen them this big. The rains had come and fallen at just the right time and in just the right place for big juicy berries.

When he was lifted from the troopie and placed on the

ground, one of the babies stumbled after the bigger kids, stumpy little legs trying hard to keep up. Big brother came back, picked him up and swung him onto his shoulders. Off they went with baby's hand clutching the battered, enamelled pannikin that bounced off the curly hair of his big brother.

Small groups of finches flew out from the shelter of the bushes to land high on the branches of nearby gums and, as the wind was pushed from around their wings, it sounded like a mini-storm. They alighted there in the bushes, little feathered heads twisting and turning as if to locate the new disturbance, being careful to keep watch, seeing who had taken over the bushes. Their tails flicked and twitched, and I could hear an occasional snap of beaks. Their chirping hung over that place. As the birds watched from their lookout above, the kids spread themselves between the bushes and started to pick the fruit.

'Oi, hey. You mob should see the size of this one.'

'Yeah, this one too big.'

'You got some over there, Bubba?'

'Too many, too many, eh.'

'My cup full nearly … already.'

'Who got some for Aunty?'

'Any more cup in the motorcar?'

'That empty bottle my one. I'll fill it for Aunty.'

Voices darted in back-and-forth delight.

'Oi, slow down swallowing them. You know what will

happen if you eat too many, and don't make too much noise,' one of the grannies call-whispered back. Her voice swooped like a hawk into a gap in the delight and perched there as a reminder. And a silence spread across the little clearing.

Then, like the flock of birds ascending into the sky, the laughter rose from a scattering of mamugujama bushes, sending the last of the finches off to find their next resting place, but it fell almost immediately to a soft humming chuckle. I imagined the children were seeing the consequences of too many mamugujama but they remembered, too, that they were not to disturb the old people in this place with loud voices. The children knew things happened when the old people were disturbed.

'Mmm, yes, Gowja.' One lone quiet voice responded to Granny on behalf of all the children.

Smiling to myself, I walked off a bit, feeling my heels break through the hard crust into the soft dirt below, trailing my hand through the short, crisp leaves to grasp the sweet berries. The soft almost-prickle of the nearly there thorns on the stem of the bush was a small price to pay. This place was contained by hills far enough away for us to name it a secret valley, because it took some local knowledge to find it and at its centre was a large open space. A nice little plain. The dry dust felt good between my toes and so I continued to walk.

Rolling a single berry between my fingers, I smoothed

the skin to a polish and flicked it into my mouth. The taste squirted onto my palate and ran down the back of my throat and my memory ran back to a different place, a long time ago.

* * *

With my dad, that day after the bore work, we'd raced the turkeys to get to a mamugujama bush. It was in the desert, not here on our country. We had been cautious when we approached. Dad had been extra careful to talk to that place and to assure the old people there that we were coming to gather some food, and to let them know who we were and where we had come from. He went on to tell them we meant no harm and we would take only enough to feed us on that day, that our country and our people, like us, were grateful to be given food there. We would leave enough to share with the turkeys that would arrive soon, he assured those who dwelt there. And they were kind to us. We had enough to satisfy our needs, but it was always like that. Talk to the country, talk to old people, talk, talk, talk. Talk your story into this place to sit there with the ancestors.

Those mamugujama, they were small back then, at that other place — not like here at our place. That black soil country was dry, and everything had to use what little water it had, wisely, or perhaps that country didn't want us to know the secrets living in its water. Here, there is no secret, we have plenty of water because when my dad's mob say, 'ngurruwani Gudanji-marndi maga guda gurijba iligirra gamamjani', they are reminding us all indeed that we Gudanji are from those hills and fresh water. And that water stays with us just as we stay close to it. That water that came here with those women feeds us like it feeds the rivers and creeks on our place. Water lies in many places across our country if you know the secrets told in the stories.

My memories of me and my dad racing with the turkeys faded for a moment like the noise from the kids, and I walked on. I arrived at the foot of a small hill, where the trees grew thicker, and the shade was degrees cooler than out in the sun. Breaths of cool air floated from further back in the trees. I followed and soon came to the spring, but the smell of water beckoned me further. I sat and washed my face and arms, and carefully dripped the sweat from my face and armpits into the water. As I talked softly to the old people, my body became focused and preoccupied with greeting, so I swirled the water, laden with my sweat, adding to the smells that already occupied it. The water did its job and carried the water filtered through my body to rejoin with its memory.

I felt it, said it, thought it and then I breathed and shared my greeting, our greeting, our memory living with water and hill country. Into my lungs came the scents that live with the trees, the air that has journeyed from the very beginning until it came into me in that moment. Like a fisherman drawing in a net of fish, memories brought me into a future past where all Gudanji were gathered. In that ethereal place that is so solid in my knowing, I shared some time with my grandmother – I always did – and assured her we were all okay and shared some news of my dad. I asked if the mad kids and their mamugujama collecting were making too much noise, and, in that other place, we laughed together at how excited they were about the berries.

I sat by the water in the shade of the trees, gazing out at the spread of family on that little plain. I knew we had gathered here so many times in the past. This place was covered in small mounds of chipped and broken stone where family had forever tapped at stone shards to produce the tools, knives and spear tips that were needed, that we still used. And the bushes grew in a large sprawling oval as if landscaped by our desire for mamugujama and our incessant gathering in the company of turkeys. Generation after generation of Gudanji had sat here, making stone tools while watching the kids vie with the finches and turkeys to get the best of the mamugujama, breathing the air that still swirled here around us all.

I heard a voice calling to the kids and stood up to see what was going on. Another voice now, also calling the names of various children, and I walked quickly from the shade. At the other end of our little valley, I saw the kids, five of them, steadily climbing the hill. As I started running I heard others calling for the kids to come back. It was clear that they were within hearing distance but none of them stopped. Without any hesitation at all, they carried on up the hill. Rick was running too, scrambling up behind them, getting increasingly closer, calling to them to stop. No one did; they just continued at the same pace, up towards the top of the hill. When he reached the child who was trailing behind the others and touched his shoulder, all the kids stopped and looked around. They seemed to be startled that the adults were all at varying stages up the hill and all shouting at them.

'What are you doing?' one asked.

'Where were you going?' from someone else.

'Why are you climbing this hill?' asked another.

'Why didn't you stop?'

Between the voiced concern, their story slowly emerged and coalesced simply to, 'We were just walking ... and we couldn't stop.'

We all walked to the top and showed them what came after. The hills lined up like reflections in mirrors, all the same as far as we could see, all the same brown with the stories washed out or lying in there, deep and hidden. It was an ominous sight. We told the kids those hills were like that all the way to Elliott, to the south-west. It was dry country. Only the old travellers walked there,

When we were back at the bottom of the hill, sitting around the fire, Aunty asked the kids what had happened to cause them to climb the hill and close their ears.

'And what happened to you mob? Where you all been walking? You know why you all been going up the hill? 'Cause you should have stayed at the mamugujama bushes. Who reckon you can go walk up that hill? You don't know this place yet. You only little ones.'

And then Aunty started to tell stories about the old days, when she was a kid and what her aunties and grannies had told her about this place.

'Them old people been here long time, you know. They been sitting here in this place and they been making all this thing. All them mamugujama. All them stones, smooth ones, sharp ones – they made them all. Must be they been sitting here long time, all the time waiting for you mob. That's true, you know, they still here. You mob gotta listen to them old people. That's the ones who been taking you. They telling you to listen. They must be seen your ear shut 'cause you don't listen. They taking you in the desert, make you sit down until your ear can open up then it can listen.'

All the kids looked about them as they were told about the old people sitting in this place. They looked, while carefully keeping eyes averted from their grand-mother's, but also from any of the old people who they might see sitting with them. Their gaze ran across the ground, checking. A silent stillness sat with the kids as they all carefully turned over the words and then, with their deep breathing, that place seemed to sigh and turn back to peace.

One of the kids asked their granny, 'Can we eat some more mamugujama now then, Mimi?'

'Did you hear what I told you?'

With barely discernible nods back and forth, the kids decided that it was time to return to the bushes for the sweet fruit. They would stay inside the round growth of bushes and not go past the outer perimeter. The turkeys would have plenty of the plump purple-brown berries on the outside. There would be no more venturing beyond the base of the hill.

A pounding

The sun was still dozing behind the hills far off towards the coast, but its light was making its way across the country. Already people were awake, fires flaring into low flames to warm themselves around, and the children played and watched for the lizards that were still too cold to move swiftly. Some of the older kids were looking down onto the flat to see if there were any turkeys nearby. They peered through the shadowed light to try to find the mobs of kangaroos that were often feeding on the soft fresh grass growing down there near a soak. It was a peaceful enterprise, until one of them noticed a strange movement in the distance that was neither kangaroo nor turkey. Others looked and watched, and they soon understood that it was not of this place.

'Ngajba! Look!' the children cried, as they stood in the early morning on the flat-top hill. Looking into the far distance at the strange dark shadow as it ran across the land like a black waterless tide.

'Ngajba!' they cried again, pointing little fingers, some with grease from their breakfast of leftover turkey, as that black tide raced towards them. On a breath of wind came a rolling sound, thudding and pounding. The sound was wild, like a heartbeat worried with fear, and it came with the dry acrid smell of mourning.

'Ngajba!' And the tide separated into four-legged beasts with their shadows sliding furiously beneath, running fast across the earth. Dust rose behind the galloping beasts and hung in the early morning air. It clung to the overnight damp like red flags waving danger to the children watching from the hillside.

Adults rose around the smouldering early-morning fires and kicked dust to smother the smoke. Bones from the evening meal were kicked into the ash and dirt. String bags gathered and hung from shoulders, small children placed on shoulders, and the group melted as one into a fast jog as it headed towards the distant rising rock face of Garranjini.

Dust rose around the many pairs of ankles of that family. It hung there, still and mute, as the irra moved resolutely and silently across the rocky space. The dust tried to cling to the moving heels but slid back onto the stones and dirt, into the soft indentations left by the hurrying feet. Prints faded to almost nothing and the slight morning breeze moved the dust to hide the tracks. The earth glowed red as the sunlight filtered through its shadows of dust, and the light that was cast found all the minute details. Heels hardened through the continuous meeting and parting with earth, split in places to mirror the gorges in the landscape in which they walked, secreted away specks of red. The hurrying footfalls continued, echoing the heartbeat of the walkers, and picked up those other echoes they'd heard from the fire. And perhaps the heart and the feet reminded each other of that old rhythm and pondered the strange, awful coming.

No one wasted time looking behind them, to trace the sound. They felt it inside, growing up through the earth to surround them as they hurried across the ground. The light became sharper and the foliage seemed to shrink; comfort was stripped away. They moved forward, carefully listening through the pounding felt by their feet to the urgent messages arranging themselves underneath. As they crossed country, the sound from beyond the valley came to them again. The jarring ring of metal against rock glanced off the earth and leapt from surface to surface. Steps quickened without a word being uttered and dust was given even less chance to cling to passing heels that were now moving in a desperate run above the fine, spilt red powder.

'Mankujba!' came the whispered directive. 'Mankujba!'

And, as they listened, they ran. Again they heard that

strangely voiced ring uttered from that awful thing, carried on soft wind. They felt the smell of those four-legged beasts creep into their noses, bringing a strange sweat this country didn't know. And another knowing came with it. These were the marndaji and they followed no law from this country.

Mankujba! And the old people talked.

As irra continued on an unmarked path, seen and known only to them, there was little evidence left of their passage. Stones and grass and trees and walkers all renewed their kinship and spoke to each other in tongues unvoiced and unheard. Of the same earth and all of the same kin. Silence, their companion, embraced them. The trees and the breeze sang quietly together and muffled the whispered voices as they passed.

Across the valley, stones screeched, violently displaced from a resting place that had been so for an unimaginable time. They rattled and groaned, and the irra across the valley heard wildness and death in that sound as it came into their ears. And still echoing through the stones' rattle could be heard that terrible ringing. The ringing that lengthened and became louder and the thud of the heels whispered fearfully back. Bardba! Run away! Bardba! Bardba!

During those moments, as heel, metal and rock uttered, when voices from long ancient pasts and those from faraway shores mingled, and the wind sighed, seventeen people noiselessly slid down into the valley through a long and deep abyss close to Garranjini. They had passed from the light now hitting the red rock face onto soft spongy ground made that way by eons of foliage dropping to form a floating mat of composting matter. The decomposing leaf litter greeted the feet, sinking a little to fill with the water from beneath, only to reshape and hide the path when the feet had passed.

And as the sun began to slide away in the west, shadows that had been running to catch irriyani now caught up. Fear of the lawlessness infusing the landscape came with the shadows to walk across the country and left scars that could not be smoothed over by the wind. The earth tried to swallow the fear, as irriyani had also been swallowed, but the awful ringing noise continued across the valley.

'Bardba, bardba...' The voices, in their urgency, floated to waiting ears. 'Run away, get away ... and find a quiet still place.' And, like the voices, the dust particles settled back into their place.

The sun threw cruel light on both ngarrinji and dust. It mocked that family and their faith in that place. They saw light spreading across the land, but it soon become lost in the trees. The voices were gone but their echo had travelled and, perhaps, was heard.

Feet continued to journey across the earth, through the valley. They travelled swiftly and silently, touching the earth softly, tenderly, in a rapid greeting and a swifter goodbye. For all that could be seen, those feet might never have crossed there. As if an earthly conspiracy to cover and conceal the passing of people into an ancient sacred space, the dust was lifted by the wind to shroud the marks left by their heels.

The unknown noise faded and became lost in the embrace of the valley. As that foreign sound disappeared, the earth seemed to take a breath and gather itself, preparing for what might be yet to come. Irriyani continued to the place they could see a short distance ahead, where the trees were giants and the water ran clear – Garranjini.

They stopped in a small cave that stood high on the sloping side of the valley. The entrance could be overlooked if you didn't know it was there. They entered the shelter, each offering their greeting to the ancestors and old people who protected and still lived in that place. They wiped small, rounded stones with the perspiration from their bodies and spoke softly the words to remember kinship, then dropped the stones into the water pooling at the side of the cave.

One of the nayida took some water and mixed it with white powder she had taken from a small kangaroo-skin pouch tied to her waist. She stirred until it became a thin paste, then took the mixture to the wall of the cave.

There, in front of her, were patterns in white and red. She lifted her white-tipped finger and slowly traced over the marks already there. One, two, three lines all side by side, all the same, upwards, along the wall. Then, one, two, three lines all side by side, all the same, across, along the cave floor. She traced two sets of those lines on either end of the first three. As she painted, she sang for the women who would come to this place a long time from now; she sang them each by name. And as she sang, she breathed the thudding of the four-legged beasts and their riders away from this place, away from her yet-to-become family.

She could not allow the thought that, for some awful reason, the creatures atop the beasts would take her future family and that those women would not make the marks again with hands that were not hers but that were of her. She continued to sing softly into the walls and the paint, making marks in the present so the future could live. Just as the previous hands had marked this place and all the others like it — the task was for the nayida in her line — it would be continued.

The white marks stood against the red of the wall and, when she finished, she was satisfied. The marks showing her mob this country, mapping this country, where water was to be found and identifying her in those water places, were complete.

As she stood back and viewed the marks, my granny wondered for a moment at those future women and considered what their landscapes might be. She hoped that through these marks in a small cave, on an even smaller cave wall, those women would understand and know this place. She hoped they could trace the journey that linked them to this country. Many secret waterholes across Gudanji lands were marked with signs of her, of my grandmother's moment of being there. And those signs stretched back, were linked through time, to the beginning, when those three Water-women first danced this Country into being and placed the first marks on that earth wall.

My granny didn't need to worry too much. My children and I have walked, and continue to walk, across Gudanji Country, into the marks of her feet. And now we walked up the side of the hill into the damp cave. We all looked at and gently touched the marks on its wall. My daughters and my son all wear her mark on their arms. Their tattoos are not sentimental displays of reminiscence; they are the celebration of family and Country and relationship. They each decided to get the tattoo as a privilege of identity with Gudanji Country, through my father and his mother, my granny. My elder daughter said she hoped her nanna wouldn't mind, but that she wasn't tough enough to do the whole scarring thing. A tattoo is mild compared with that older process. My granny's marks were cicatrices created through the ongoing cutting of flesh and filling with ash. She spilled her blood into this country while taking this country – the ash – into her body to *become* with it.

Crocodiles and bullocks

The small group who heard the metal ringing out was made up of Bungmaji and his six grown children. Bungmaji lived the stories passed down from the old people and knew about staying with country, about following the right paths. He knew, too, that things were changing, that his family had to travel to another country to be safe. This choice was not taken lightly; it was simply a matter of life or death. The fear was not the immediate ending of their life; rather, it was the possible end to his yet-to-come family and to their future that demanded such rapid movement across the earth, to leave Gudanji Country. Things were changing but things were changing around the irra — not with them, not for them.

On his back, Bungmaji carried one of his sons. He had been born crippled but Bungmaji had refused to put the baby to death, as was often the practice. He had taken responsibility for providing the livelihood by which his son had survived. The old man had carried him now for some eighteen years and the responsibility was shared throughout the family.

Just a handful of days ago Bungmaji had seen his sister tied to a tree. The flies that fed off her ripped and torn flesh had hung above her like a smoke haze and their buzzing hung there too. The day before the flogging, she had been dragged to that tree, wrists placed in a pair of iron cuffs and left with neither food nor water. She had refused to cry out and so had been flogged for a time longer. Those who took turns grasping the whip had laughed and used extra force to see who could make her scream the loudest. They had laughed as her bared breasts, now shining with sweat and spots of blood, jumped and shook with each of the blows from the whip. She had refused to give them the satisfaction of hearing her pain, so just as none of them heard her screams during the day neither did they hear her muffled moans of agony at night as her family tended the wounds.

Their family from over the other side, towards the sunup country, had told them already about the evil that lived there now, about the collection of ears this evil had pinned to the walls of his shelter. They had told them about the blood that soaked and dripped there now, where once there was only the fresh water of Boodjamulla.

It had frightened Bungmaji deeply to see the horrors

of what they were doing. His nephew had been shot just recently too. Ngajimji had been down by the river when he saw a crocodile attack a bullock. The teeth of the crocodile latched onto the bullock and pulled and pulled. The soft nose of the bullock ensured the crocodile had an easy task of dragging the beast to the edge of the water. As the kicking and thrashing and half-drowned bellows of the bullock mixed with mud and clotting blood in the boiling water, final gasps of air escaped, and the bullock was dead.

The beast was too big for the crocodile to drag too far and so the reptile started to eat it there, as it lay half in, half out of the water. The opportunity for meat was never wasted, so ngajimji started to slice the back leg from the bullock while the crocodile feasted on the head. As ngajimji hoisted the fresh meat to his shoulder, riders from the nearby station came to the high riverbank. Seeing him with the beef, they simply took aim and fired. Although his ngajimji was a big man, he was neither slow nor weak. He dropped the leg of beef – perhaps the crocodile ate it after all – and he ran and ran.

They found his body a long way from the river. One of the bullets that had been fired had reached Bungmaji's ngajimji and, when they found him, the hole of the bullet had been through his goodalu.

Red tinted many things that day. The blood from his ngajimji coloured the surrounding earth and soaked into the already blood-red dirt. The dust lost its weightlessness and covered irra and that place. When irriyani gathered to see where his ngajimji had lain, the sweat gathering on their faces mixed with the dust and ran as tears. But it might be that those tears were from the earth and not irriyani, because the tears, on that day, ran red.

That place had become just like the place where the old people went to gather the sacred red and white ochre at ceremony time. When the family collected his ngajimji and took him away from the river, across his face, as if painted for ceremony, was smeared the red ochre that wasn't ochre. The face of his ngajimji was painted in a new and different ochre. So much death, so much pain and so much suffering. Where was the end of it all? They had come and taken country and it seemed they were still not satisfied.

Bungmaji feared the effects upon his sons. They would surely expect payback for the treatment of their sisters, mothers, aunties and grandmothers, and he knew the skilfully made weapons, the spears and nulla-nullas, would cause little real harm against the rifles carried by the others. Gudanji had limited weaponry that was capable of killing a fellow human being; Gudanji chose only weapons that allowed them to gather food. He knew, too, that the killer boomerang would not stand up well against the guns of those who now travelled this country. He feared the effects on his daughters, but he was terrified for his children who were to be born into this place far into the future.

Talking good way

Not so long before that, the rainbow in the sky lost its way when the colours cried together to become an indistinct grey mass.

A meeting, they said, come to a meeting. We will talk about this country. We will talk straight about what might happen here, they said. We will talk good way. We will talk about us two mobs here now and how we can live here together, they said. But they lied.

Storymen from all the languages in Gulf Country went to that meeting, walking with faith and the belief that we could live together. They were all there, the holders of the stories, of the ceremonies and of the law. Ten storymen went and none came back. Those who wanted the meeting, those who'd said they wanted to talk straight, to talk good way, surrounded the storymen and then their rifles talked in a tongue understood only by those rifles and by death.

The Rainmaker-men from the Gulf were no more, the colour had bled from the sky. Ceremonies stopped. Who was there with the authority to hold them? Who was there who could speak the old languages of the ancestors? Who was there to speak in the old languages of this country? Who was able to call to the colours in the rainbow and build the rains that the Gulf Country needs? Gudanji, like the other people of the Gulf, turned to Country and listened more deeply to the secrets travelling on the wind and through all the kin who shared Gudanji space, to recall the knowing, to keep the goodalu and the kujiga.

Home

Garranjini had always kept the Gudanji safe. The huge pool of water surrounded by the giant paperbark trees was a place few others ventured into. It was Gudanji Country. The Dreaming made it that way. This was where the three Water-women stopped. They had journeyed through all the country and were heading back out to the sea, the way they came. At Garranjini they called up the water with the salt because, after travelling in the southern desert country, they were full of sickness for their home. They called to the ocean and the ocean came. And then they danced and sang. The marks of that great body of water coming to Garranjini are still there for people to see. The dish in the side of the gorge, made when the water came pouring over, where the ocean broke away the rock, still directs the water at that place.

The alien sound of metal against rock rang out again

and the old man was drawn from his memories. The group in the shelter of the gorges heard the noise of metal drawing nearer. *They* were drawing nearer. The group walked quickly to the gorge wall. As they drew closer, they were particularly careful to make as little sign of their presence as possible. Closer they went until, silently, like the most fleeting of shadows, they disappeared into the almost invisible split in the wall of the gorge. They could wait there and be safe for a time. They could rest and eat and prepare for the next day's walk. The group settled in the shaded and protected chasm. The modest fire they allowed themselves warmed some of the cold from their skin. The cold within their bodies, a new and shocking cold, would require a fire much larger than they could risk that night.

The next day, while the stars were still in the sky, irriyani were again walking. By the end of that day, they were in a place where people could disappear, never to return. They walked with care through the secret valley where the foothills repeated themselves so many times people forgot where they were, and families always had to remind the children to listen carefully. Stone tools had been manufactured in that place for a long, long time by fathers and sons and grandfathers all sitting there with the stones.

They replenished supplies of tools as they walked through that place and if it were another time of year, the sweet, fat mamugujama would have given them some extra food for their journey. Walking in the shadows of the hills, away from where eyes could see, they watched carefully where they were going and who might be coming. They were travelling through their mother's country, of the Mudburra people.

Bungmaji spent his walking time with more memories and took himself to the time when the old people travelled upriver to make dugout canoes. They would go just as the winds from the south came. The knock-'em-down winds on that country told everyone that rain would be coming soon. He remembered when they'd travelled upriver, to where the big paperbarks grew, and how long it took to cut down a tree and then the long job of making it hollow.

All the family worked on those canoes, taking direction from the boatmaker. He would speak to the boatmakers who had been there before and ask for their guidance. And this reminded him how the canoes would always be finished just as the rains started. The river would swell within its banks and there was time to check if it worked as a boat should. The boat would be refined and then, just as the rain set in and became a monsoon, the raging river would overflow, and people would ride safe and dry in their boats back down towards the coastal plains. Bungmaji wore a sad little smile as he packed his memories away again. The people who were no longer here, the funny games he and his friends had played when they could be young, with no problems at all, made the sorrow in him bigger for what was happening now.

On and on irriyani travelled, under the familiar heat of the sun. They especially noticed changes in the trees and the grass and the earth because these changes were unfamiliar. Across the country trees were being cut down and left to die a seemingly easy and thoughtless death. They were not burned for fire, so the earth received no nourishment from the ash of the trees to grow more. The trees lay with their leafless branches reaching towards the sky, helplessly and hopelessly. They begged anyone to come closer to end their misery, to set them alight so their spirit might travel to the place where all spirits resided together and from where new life came. No longer were the forests large and protective as they used to be, just ugly, scrawny, naked branches waiting now to become dust. No words had been spoken over them as they fell to the earth, so their journey was a slow and stilted one.

The ringing sound had been left behind but all in the group knew that soon it would return. And then it would be ringing so much louder because then there would be many more of them, those new people who had come here without grace or patience and who spoke of lore and not law, were not going to leave. The ringing would fill the air and cling to the trees and run with the wind through the grass. It would invade the ears of those near enough to hear and stay there safe within the body of its carrier like a small but insistent parasite, living covertly, protected. It would be difficult to ever cut the terror out and it would continue in the bodies of those who came after. Perhaps in some it would grow and in some it might become shrivelled and in others it would become a distant memory of the terrible things that once happened to our country and to us.

Travelling

When Bungmaji's small group sat in the shelter of that lesser woodland scrub, they were visited by some of their own people from a nearby station. These people bought news of another massacre at Macarthur River — Gudanji men had attacked station people as payback for several rapes. They had surrounded the station and the people there had barricaded themselves inside the house. Although the spears did much damage to the two men caught outside, they bounced off the walls of the house itself. The next week, a posse, with the help of blacktrackers from Queensland, had encircled the Gudanji and opened fire at dawn. All but one was killed, but that lone survivor of the massacre had chosen to jump over the cliff into the gorge below rather than fall into the hands of the others.

The travellers were told that most of the flour was now being poisoned, as well as the smaller waterholes. Bungmaji remembered when he was younger and the new people would offer flour, some tea and, sometimes, sugar. More and more now, those things carried with them a death that was not natural. It was a cruel death; it whispered that flour and small waterholes were to be avoided.

Further along the journey, the group came upon the remains of a slaughtered bullock. They all looked and shared a grin. The sad and dry bones, located as they were, told their own story. Bungmaji and his family knew of other juwa who raided the stock now roaming on much of their country. Some would regularly spear and butcher a beast and have a great feast just to prove a point. This part of the country had been declared a newly established stock route and cattle were often to be found here. The juwa would come across from the surrounding hills, kill what they needed and return. One day they would be caught but for now they simply refused to let loose their place in the kinship chain. The new stock route ran along the southern side of the Gulf to take cattle from one side of the Queensland–Northern Territory border to the other.

Bungmaji and his family continued their journey heading south, now they were beyond the brown hills. They all shared the task of carrying their brother and son; they all shared the task of providing food for each other, so they all shared the responsibility for the journey to keep their future family safe.

Tomatoes and chicken

Yugala ngangaba, smoke and fire, and then wisps of white feathers floated a while in the air only to drop to the ground as the red dust eddied and churned the sky. The group of boys ran quickly away from the chook yard. Their muffled laughter followed them like the puffs of dust that followed their hastily moving feet. The chicken with its twisted neck and broken feathers lay limp in the bottom of the hessian sack being tossed between them.

'Have you got the salt?' asked one.

'Yes, and the matches,' answered another, patting a bulging pocket. 'We'd better get right down the creek 'cause manager will be after us if he sees any smoke.'

'I got tomatoes from the garden, too,' said the third boy in the group. 'Not too many, just enough. No one will notice. The pigs got in last night. They won't miss a few tomatoes.'

'Yeah, did you see what he did to Old John? Flogged with the horse whip, he was,' said the first.

'But Old John didn't leave the pig house open,' claimed the third.

'Well, he couldn't flog Miss Christine, could he? She was the one who did it.'

'Come on, this'll do. We're far enough away from the big house. Get some wood.'

As the fire took and small red and yellow flames jumped from its burning heart, the boys were careful to gather the feathers they plucked from the chicken. The chicken was cut open with an old knife one of them pulled from the pocket of the baggy green pants he wore. Entrails were tossed into the hole with the feathers, and all buried together. The chicken was opened flat and placed upon the coals now that the fire had burned away. They passed salt and tomatoes between them, chewing happily. The juice of the tomatoes ran down their cheeks and dripped onto bare chests. One of the boys leaned forward and turned the chicken as it cooked upon the glowing coals.

The thinning cotton pants soon became splattered with the juice and seeds of the tomatoes as well as the juice of the now-cooked chicken. They all wore those pants. They were like a uniform. Everyone on the station was given a pair of pants, a shirt, some tobacco and a blanket. It was payment for work, meant to keep people on the station, wanting more. The pants that the boys wore were only their first issue. Somewhere between seven and nine years old, they had been doing the work tasks of men for some time and each was now entitled to his own bundle of items handed out every six months, though it didn't mean they received what was due. The pants they wore were hand-me-downs. When they had been so well used by the older men that much of the fabric was lost, and they became more full of holes than the red ant beds that grew in that place, then the pants would be given to the young boys.

This meal was a poignant one. The three boys were all going in different directions soon. One was heading further up into the Gulf to Borroloola, the other was going to work with a drover, to be the cook's offsider going across to the border in the west, down the Murranji track, but Soda would stay here on the Tableland station. He had already made that trip and was the oldest in this group. Soda had to remain because he was doing the work of a grown man. They knew that the stations often traded workers and sometimes it was just necessary to go. Most of the time, the decision was not theirs to make; they were simply told. So their growing and sharing time and the brotherhood had come to an end.

After eating the coal-fire-roasted chicken and tomatoes from the ill-fated garden, the three boys washed carefully in the creek. All traces of the meal had to be erased. They all knew that the flogging Old John had received was nothing compared with what they would get if anyone found out about the stolen meal. The potential consequences of consuming pig-bruised tomatoes and a no-longer-laying chicken were too awful to think about.

The work on the station was hard and constant — six days a week from sunup to sundown. Mostly it remained the same but sometimes it changed, depending on the time of the year. Mustering the paddocks, drafting the cattle, the branding and the castrating and the inoculations, working in the gardens and keeping the house supplied with goods, killing a bullock and cutting it up ... on and on it went. The work was always about preparing the cattle for sale. Other jobs grew from that need — catching and breaking in horses, building and checking fences to maintain stock separation, working on the vehicles and maintaining the bores for water supply. It was always about the cattle, a never-ending cycle of work swirling around the station with the usual dust storms, and always the sails of the windmills pumping furiously in the background.

Soda's time was spent mostly in company with only his thoughts, living out and away from the station, working the bores, which in turn watered the cattle. He watched for dingos — set some traps, scalped any of them he caught and kept the salted and dried pelts rolled in an old, tattered hessian bag to be sold when he had a chance. Sometimes a hawker came by who would give him some money for them. When he had the chance to sell the pelts, he would hoard the coins in his palm and slide them into his pocket.

Soda would walk a little way off then, listening for the strangeness of the sounds made by those coins as he rattled them, making them rub and clang together. He always kept his hands in his pockets to stop the coins from slipping through any holes that might be there. Before the hawker left the station, Soda would give the money back to buy small gifts or lollies for himself and his two cousins, Katie and Peggy, but he always insisted on first getting the coins in his hand to feel the rigid, round metal sitting dry and hard in his palm, to learn the texture of money.

The arrangement of events that had led to Soda's birth was, unfortunately, too common. His mother was 'drover's boy' to a drover who left her pregnant. When Soda was born, Wilson, the old man his mother had been promised to for marriage, had quickly noticed the lighter shade of the baby's skin. That old man had beaten my granny and had made her leave the newborn, my dad, on an ant bed. It had been an unforgivable thing that Dad had been born with a lighter skin, so he had been left for the ants to remove it.

Many times, *they* came to get him, as they did all the children born with different skin, skin that came from *them*, but he had been one of very few to have stayed on the station. His uncle, his mother's brother, had protected Soda, and each time the Methodist minister came to collect the children, Uncle Paddy would cover Soda and say, 'No. This one is for me. I will grow him up for me.'

Dad vaguely remembered that time when they had

come to a remote bore some distance from the station, rounding up what they called the stray 'yella' kids. Uncle saw the dust coming a long way off and had hidden Soda. And Dad recalled holding his breath so hard that he nearly passed out as the minister walked around and stood near the bushy hiding place that was protecting him, asking Uncle about the story of the boy who lived out here at this remote bore. Uncle Paddy had murmured, as if in a confused state, 'I don't know that story, no boy like that lives here. You look there, see my boots make that mark there ... only my boots, my foot and no boy. I'm here misel'.' And Soda had watched while Uncle pointed to the marks made by the old barely together boots he insisted be tied onto Soda's feet each morning. *They* were gathering the kids to 'protect' them, they were told, but from what or who, nobody knew.

Leaving special

One day, when Soda was older, Old Scot, the bore mechanic, came and took Soda from No. 3 Bore back to the station. After he arrived, he quickly caught up with the news and new people in the camp where the Aboriginal people lived. It was a distance from the living areas of the station occupied by non-Aboriginal people. The ceremonies were due soon and there were more people than was normal at the camp. They all knew that the ceremonies were frowned on, but it was very rare that someone from the main house came to them. This was Wakaja Country, after all, and the ceremonies had always been held here. It was why everyone stayed. Soda was engrossed in the talk of ceremonies. He had heard that his mother would be there. The droving team she was with was doing the return trip so he hoped he would catch up with her. He hadn't seen her for many years now. Their parting back then was something that still caused him great pain. He recalled having got up one morning and her simply not being there. She'd run away during the night with a visiting drover, his plant of horses and all the other gear needed to complete the trip further north. He'd been happy that she'd got away from this place but for him it left a hole, an emptiness so vast it seemed bottomless.

Soda's mother played an important role in the ceremonies. As he hurried to the dance grounds, he finally caught sight of her and was incredibly happy. He was somewhat startled to see that her hair was cut so short and he thought that others had also noticed. He caught half whispers occasionally but paid no real attention. He was only glad to see her.

As the sun passed below the horizon and the emu in the heavens could be seen in the south, the sounds of the didgeridoos and boomerangs hitting one another rose into the air. Soon the dundee would be opened, people would eat the food that had been cooked in the ground ovens and the dancing would start. The old people generally managed to collect all the usual foods from the plains but this time there would be no beef. The current manager was not like past managers who had given Wakaja extra food to share with all the ceremony visitors. Goannas, kangaroos, porcupines and emus were all gathered and placed into the dundee to cook.

Soda's mother was among the first to enter the dance

circle. The sticks beat a rhythm and the didgeridoos filled the air with a sound so thick it embraced everyone. The sound wrapped around the bodies of those living still and those who were no longer there. The links with the ancestors, with the old people already gone, were strong and comforting but everyone was careful to follow the law to ensure safety. Soon, their presence could be felt in the trees and the music and the people. Into the night, the dancing continued. Fires were kept burning and, as children became sleepy, they lay on the blankets spread around the outside of the circle and went to sleep.

Something made Soda look to the side of the dance circle. There was the path that led into the area. He wasn't the only person there who had noticed someone walking along the path. Slowly, the sounds of the ceremony became mute and the dancers froze. Into the circle strode the manager and with him was his offsider. This man always carried a rifle cocked and draped over his shoulder. He was never without the old army carbine .303.

'You, Lucy,' the manager yelled, 'get out of there now. What are you doing down here anyway?' Everyone on the station called the manager Billy the Screamer because of the abuse he hurled when he wasn't brandishing a stock whip.

'I'm finished here now. I'm not here anymore. I work with the drover now. I'm not here anymore,' Lucy answered firmly.

'You don't tell me that. You're here now. Don't tell me that. Come away now. Up to the house. I want you up at the house ... now,' shouted the manager.

'I'm not here anymore,' Lucy repeated.

Soda watched this interchange along with everyone else. They all knew that the end was not going to be good. Soda moved quietly and carefully through the silent crowd and made his way to his mother's side. The crowd held its collective breath as the offsider slowly pulled the rifle from his shoulder and pointed it at Lucy.

'Come up to the house, now. I won't tell you again,' growled the manager. The threat in his voice was as audible as if he had screamed it. And perhaps it felt louder because he had not.

'No,' answered Lucy, and her voice was quiet and strong. 'I'm finished at that house.' She stared into the eye of the rifle, stood as straight as she could and waited.

People standing around the fires saw Lucy, and the embodiment of all the Gudanji women who had come and gone before her. They all saw those strong Water-women from the Dreaming standing there. As the firelight turned the white ceremonial paint to a stark vivid shroud, and her dark skin melted into the gloom, Lucy, again composed and determined, said, 'No, I'm finished at the house.' Returning to that back room in the station house and what awaited her there was not possible.

The manager exploded. He rushed at her and threw

her to the ground; he punched and kicked and bit. The offsider now had the rifle trained on the crowd. No one moved but many hands worked themselves towards spears and nulla-nullas that lay around the circle in the darkness. From her position under the heaving bulk of the Screamer, Lucy made desperate signs with her hand for the crowd to leave the weapons.

'Go, get out of here, you black heathens,' the Screamer roared at the gathered Wakaja and Gudanji people.

Lucy and the manager continued to roll around in the red dust. The rifle moved around the crowd and, on its second turn, the onlookers had disappeared, seemingly melted away in the darkness. Only Soda stood there. Soon he saw he had been mistaken and that they weren't alone. As he watched, four others stepped out from beyond the light cast by the still-dancing fire. They, too, were carrying rifles. He recognised them as the two sons of old Screamer and two jackaroos. They were all barely older than he was, and they stood there glaring at him across the flames, through the dust still being tossed into the air by the two on the ground. They glared at him as if their father, their boss, was not attacking a woman.

The Screamer yelled at his boys, 'Watch your backs, you bloody idiots, watch your backs.' The four turned and faced the darkness, rifles aimed at what they saw as black nothingness.

Soda edged forward to try to get closer and perhaps help

143

his mother but the hands of the offsider fell and grasped his shoulders. 'Hold him there,' directed the manager, now sitting astride Lucy. 'Hold him there and let him see what these black bastards are good for.' And he reached down to unbuckle his leather belt.

Six angry white men, each in his own frenzy, took turns thrashing on the ground with one horrified black woman who continued to kick and punch and scratch as best she could while being held down by hard grasping hands. The fight continued but it was a different one now. The angry words became screams that were chased and interspersed by grunts and shouts of victory – six of them. Shouts so obscene that when the filth that filled them spewed into the air, the breeze stilled and refused to pick them up and help them fly free. Instead, the breeze ensured the wickedness dropped to the ground, and sat in the dirt.

At the fight's end, dust, blood and other bodily fluids congealed and rotted under the weight of the dry cold air. It was too ugly a violence to be embraced by this country, and so *they* tightened belts and straightened moleskin pants and shared an evil noise that might be called laughter. Then, as a group, they turned to strut back to the main house on the station. Back to where their women, sipping sherry and port, sat and talked about the difficulty of training the blacks to be reliable workers. Where those women worried about the cleanliness of the washing and the weevils in the flour and pretended to not understand the ongoing births of *half-caste* children.

Before the sun rose the next morning, those who had gathered for the ceremonies had all left. Lucy had spent what was left of the night camped under the truck of the drover. As first light spread across the plain country, the drover moved his plant further north. With the plant and the drover went Lucy. She stopped and spoke to Soda before she left.

'They won't let you come with me. But you leave here, you go from here now,' his mother told him.

He could no longer stay at the station; it was now much less safe. She was dressed again in the clothes she had worn the other day, the same man's long pants and shirt that all the cattlemen wore. A hat was pulled down over her head and she could have been any of the men who worked for the drover. She was back where she had been before becoming pregnant with Soda. This drover was his father. She was again the drover's boy, riding horses and working cattle during the day, and expected to take care of the drover at night.

Bleeding

She could see the Bedford truck in the far distance. It reflected the glare of the sun and the plains were a gentle red in the dust haze. The Hereford mob roamed slowly across the land, grazing as they went. There were four others on horseback that she could see. The drover was the only one missing. He had gone ahead to check on the river and where the best watering place might be. Concern for the cattle was at the start and the end of it all.

Lucy watched as the sun hit the shining coats of the horses. This drover had only coloured horses in his plant. The two-toned chestnut and white animals looked strange to Lucy, though they still moved like the others. She'd seen them before, the last time she worked for this drover, and had thought the same then. That time was before she'd had Soda. She'd left this drover to give birth to Soda on the banks of the river, where all Wakaja babies were born, and, in this case, a Gudanji one.

A bullock broke from the mob and made off. Lucy kicked the horse she sat astride and gave chase. The beast ran faster with the horse pursuing it, but it didn't go too far. They never did. These were solid bullocks, and they liked a slower pace. As the heat rose and danced over the plains, the mob continued their slow ambling way across the dry country. Their lowing murmurs became a soothing rumble that sank into the yellow grass. The rains had been good, and the grass was plentiful for the cattle, but it would only last for a while before more drovers and their great mobs came through, trampling, destroying the goanna and porcupine holes as they went.

She was glad these were Herefords, and she could sit almost still on the horse. The pain between her legs was constant and the movement of a galloping horse increased it. She'd already replaced one small bundle of rags, needed for the bleeding that increased each time the horse accelerated. Easing into a more comfortable position, she followed the cattle across the plains and into the distance. She hoped that Soda was planning to leave that place soon. It was no longer the safe place it had been when she and her sister had gone there from their home in the north.

Ministers and babies

It was hard for him to say goodbye to his mother this time. They hadn't had much of a relationship from the start. After he had been left, as a newborn baby, on the gravelled mound of a red meat-ant nest, Soda had been lifted to safety by his aunt. She became his mother. Soda became Jemima's son. He would always respect and love Jemima for that.

Old Paddy, his uncle, also claimed him as his own son and protected him because a 'coloured' or 'yella' child, like Soda, was often removed by those who came to the station for just that purpose. Soda and any other such children were often painted with charcoal to darken their skin. And when the need arose, Old Paddy always covered Soda with a shield, ever careful to keep the not-dark-enough, not-light-enough baby from sight. No one dared to lift Paddy's shield. It was a tool for fighting and very few willingly made to challenge Old Paddy.

Like his sister, Soda's mother, Paddy was a fine Tableland stick fighter, but he wielded the killer boomerang much better. There'd even been whispered stories about him cutting the kidneys and sometimes the liver from one of *them*, a man who had raped Paddy's mother. It was Gudanji practice to remove the kidneys and liver from the bodies of men who practised cruelty against them. It ensured that that spirit was never able to make its way back to their bodies, that the wickedness could not regrow. Even the Methodist minister, who regularly visited the camp and assisted in the removal of children such as Soda, never lifted Old Paddy's shield. And so the boy grew up in the camp with his own family, despite the many attempts, all too frequently successful, to remove the 'coloureds' from the landscape.

His cousins, who were older, later told him of the fear and the deep sadness that lived at that place back then, and the different fear and sadness that followed. They told him how the Methodist minister would often collect the babies but never take them into his car as he drove off the station. They told him of the places that showed newly turned earth after his visits and how the cries of the babies would be carried in the middle of the night, to quickly fade and be gone.

Brownies and damper

Dust plumed behind the vehicle as it travelled over the loosely gravelled track. The mirages danced in the distance, but the heat also boldly invaded the Land Rover cab and occupied that space, uninvited. I sat there on the cracked vinyl seat, moving with the rocking vehicle, sweating but happy to be with Bimbo, my most favourite person in the whole entire world … after my nanna but before my horse Gypsy.

I often stayed with Nanna and Bimbo out bush on Herbert Vale. I always had to finish all my schoolwork first but, once that was done, I was off for holidays with Nanna and Bimbo. I really liked my correspondence schoolwork with its one week's worth of lessons contained in a single book, all the subjects together. I could complete three and sometimes four weeks in one week, which meant I could go and do other things, important things, with Nanna and Bimbo.

Nanna and I would bake a brownie every so often – the Australian bush version, not what people call brownies now. We would mix flour and baking soda with some fat, rendered from the killer, and a small handful of dried mixed fruit. Then we'd mix in a cup of water with some syrup in it and cook the batter in the camp oven. The day it was cooked, we'd eat it with a cup of tea at suppertime for dessert. Bimbo preferred to eat brownie at smoko time. Nanna taught me to do fancywork when the moon was shining. She had taught Mum, too, to do that beautiful embroidery under the moon. I always thought it was because it looked lovely to be sewing by moonlight, but I realised later that this was most likely to be the only time she had to do something for pure enjoyment – stolen time stitched into that delicate embroidery on scraps of clean and cherished linen cloth.

Bimbo and I often drove around in the old station Land Rover, checking the working of bores and the lives of cattle. Because Herbert Vale was located on a particularly dry block of border country, the cattle often had dry spells, when water was so scarce that we sometimes carried 44-gallon drums filled with the stuff, to give some of the wretched beasts enough that they might walk to the next bore, where there could be water in the trough but just as likely not. I remember when the drought was so bad that cattle gathered around our house, but we had barely enough water for ourselves and so each morning there would be more carcasses lying in the paddock. At that time, when I said I was thirsty, Nanna would carefully measure several mouthfuls of water into a cup and what I didn't drink, she would save or, if she was thirsty, drink herself. She and Bimbo often went without. We could only bathe twice a week, so the old iron tub would be half filled with water. We washed our clothes first, then I would bathe, then Nanna and then it would be Bimbo's turn, and then Nanna would wash his clothes.

Then the water that was left, stained red brown, would be tipped onto the few lucerne shrubs we'd grow for our chickens and one very lonely but precious tomato plant that had only ever given about five tomatoes. That plant represented so much more than the pleasure of having a slice of fresh tomato with the corned beef. That plant was hope: in those drooping, barely alive leaves on its stunted vine, we saw possibility and anticipation, mostly of rain but perhaps, too, of other things. Even now, years later, I can't bear to pour undrunk water down the sink, and the dripping of taps brings on acute anxiety. It is strange how that continues to affect me, whereas the time when the Wet had dropped so much water that the roads were impassable for ages, when my mum and dad desperately managed to convince the station manager to make a food drop for us from a plane, is just a memory ... There was too much water then.

Diesel was also precious, so Bimbo would build a death

pile, the carcasses of cattle that continued to rot and eventually dry, until it was large enough to be set alight and burned with some of the precious diesel. Fortunately, because it was so dry, we didn't often notice the stench of the death pile, but the mummified cattle with their leathered skin made grotesque garden ornaments in the parched paddock that we overlooked when we sat down to eat dinner.

And Bimbo made cake tins for me. Nanna and I loved to open a tin of herrings in tomato sauce and eat it with our own baked bread for breakfast. Bimbo would then fashion mini cake tins for my brownies out of the empty tins, and he would make beautiful wooden beds for my two dolls, using pieces of carefully cut floor vinyl for the mattress bases. Every Saturday night, I would mostly read, Nanna would stitch and Bimbo would listen to *Ranch Club*, the country music hour played over the wireless.

Herbert Vale was isolated, and the road out there travelled over a bit of a plain from which dust would rise, signalling the impending arrival of visitors. We had a rooster who would crow whenever a vehicle was coming, even in advance of the dust. Big Red would strut around the thirsty yard, scratching at the dirt to find only more dirt, but he would scratch so hard that clouds of dust from his wickedly thorned spurs would be tossed high into the air. The only time our rooster crowed was to tell us that, soon, we would have visitors but sometimes he would sit under the five stairs into the house to ambush the arrivals.

I think Dad liked the isolation of that place because, to get to us, visitors mostly had to go through Rocklands, the station that he worked on, so he always knew who was coming to Herbert Vale.

Dad and Nanna were friends. They both spoke Wakaja, and they would often talk quietly together, without sharing that yarning with anyone else. It was as if it was their secret. I expect it was also just so ordinarily comforting to be able to speak easily and freely, in your own language, with someone else who also belonged to that language. I think they'd decided to stay quiet about their shared language because they could protect each other better like that. And it was a very unlikely alliance, because Nanna was so very fair-skinned and grandmotherly, and few people recognised her as Wakaja, and she certainly never spoke of her identity, and Dad was a young dark-skinned man, whom nobody would consider to be anything other than Aboriginal. Nanna liked Dad and Dad liked Nanna, and they had chosen each other as friends for themselves and not because of Mum and Dad's marriage. Dad always valued anyone who watched out for Mum, and Nanna certainly did that. So, in my growing, I got to be nurtured by Nanna and Bimbo, my great-grandparents, mostly while they were at Herbert Vale.

Arid places

Bimbo and I had been driving for many hours and the early morning light had long changed into the searing heat of midday, with the sun overhead sending out a clean hot light that cast a silver sheen over the surrounding countryside. Bimbo looked at me as I hung my arm out the window, spreading my fingers into the wind, letting the wind lift my arm with its pressure. Occasionally I could snatch a leaf when the vehicle veered near a tree or bush that had grown closer to the track.

'Careful, Bub, something might be in those bushes. A stick might spear you.' And then he said the words guaranteed to make me pull my hand back — 'Or there might be a spider.'

My hand was inside again in an instant and I looked at him to try to work out if he was kidding me or not. He wore the smile he always had on his face. It was a kind of inscrutable but also comforting smile that comes from a deeply personal level of in-my-skin comfort and, as I looked closely, the glint in his eyes twinkled at me. My hand crept back to the window opening and he said, his eyes back on the twisting road, 'Spiders, Bub,' and his smile stilled. I placed my hand on my lap and said nothing.

The vehicle continued along the track and over a dip that left the sparsely treed gully and rose to a rocky ridge. Towards the south and to the east I could see forever but there was some gidgea growing further to the north that made it impossible to see where Herbert Vale would be, far off in the distance.

'Are you thirsty, Bub?'

'Yes, Bimbo. It's very hot, isn't it?'

'Mmm, a bit warm. Are you hungry, Bub?

'Mmm, a bit hungry, Bimbo.' We had snacked on the sandwiches Nanna packed for us that morning and neither of us could bring too much interest to eating the last of the damper and corned beef. It would be starting to dry out by now but it would still be enough to feed any hunger that came visiting. And it was just too hot to eat the fruitcake.

'Do you feel like eating a fish?'

He was back to teasing me now because we were so far from any water, even our house water tank wouldn't support a fish and we had been carefully sipping from the waterbag at the front of the Land Rover, rationing the contents. There was also a canteen of water on the back of the Land Rover that would be boiling by now but would get us out of trouble if need be. I knew there wasn't anywhere within half a day's drive where we could get a fish and there was no way we would drive down to Camooweal to catch one in the Georgina.

Playing along, I answered, 'Yes Bimbo, I'd like ... maybe two fish for dinner', leaving a dramatic pause in the middle as I pretended to consider how many fish would slake my hunger, and then I laughed. We ate dinner at midday and supper at night and I don't know if it was a leftover from Nanna's Scottish heritage or Methodist practice, but, in those days, we didn't eat lunch.

He laughed too. 'Well, what about a nice cool drink of water to go with them two fish?'

I looked at him and wondered what was going on, because he didn't normally take the joke this far. He was still grinning and gave a little chuckle as he pulled the vehicle to the side of the road atop a slight rocky ridge.

'Put your hat on or Nanna will be growling at me when we get home tonight.'

As we both got out of the vehicle I looked around, trying to see some water where we could catch some fish, but it was the same as the last time we'd passed through this place. Hot and arid. I'd read that word in my schoolwork recently – it was a good word. I enjoyed the way it tasted in my mouth – just growing in there and then pushed out on a breath. *Arid* ... it meant dry and barren, I had read, and you used it to talk about land. Yes, it was definitely arid at this place.

'Where's the water, Bimbo? We need water to get fish,' I reminded him in case he'd spent too much time in the sun. It was easy to do out in this arid place. And there were no fishing lines in the Land Rover anyway or clouds in the sky; I knew fish could sometimes be dropped from just the right kind of clouds.

'Come on, I'll show you.' And off he went, walking to a large flattish rock sitting near a washout, still chuckling. He quietened then, stood still and silent beside the rock and looked around, watching approximately where the road led into the distance, behind us and in front, and I could hear words being spoken under his breath. Bimbo was Kalkadoon and he'd taught me some of that language. I still wasn't very good but knew that was what he was murmuring. I looked in the direction he looked and could see nothing, no dust, nothing that wasn't there the last time we passed here. It was all the same pale dry green that bled into the pale dry landscape.

He was satisfied with what he saw and bent down, crouched over the rock. As I watched, he moved the rock and then lay flat on the ground. I walked closer and peered down at him. What was going on? Had he suddenly become unwell? Could I remember how to drive the vehicle? But how could I lift him into it? There were so many questions and confused thoughts running through my head that it took a moment for me to notice the hole that Bimbo was lying beside — the hole in the ground that he now threaded his arm into.

I crouched beside him and put my head to the ground, trying to see into the hole.

'Don't knock any dirt in now, Bub,' he said. 'Can you get the pannikin out of the truck for me?'

I didn't want to leave the hole in the ground because I could smell water now. The scent of clean fresh water stole into my nose and I imagined I could feel its softness against my skin the way I felt the cooling cloth that Nanna wiped my face with whenever I was sick. I looked at Bimbo and scrambled to my feet and ran to the Land Rover to get the mug. I ran fast because I didn't want to miss this amazing thing that was happening here. Cool water, it seemed, was a definite possibility.

Bimbo dipped the pannikin into the hole in the ground and, as he handed it up to me, a few drops of water fell into the dirt. I watched the water fall in slow motion to the ground and hit the dirt with a minute splash of dust. And then it formed a tiny puddle that almost immediately turned into a hollow fairy dish of drying mud and, as it dried into a smooth shiny surface, it became like chocolate. I took the mug to my face and again breathed in the scent of fresh water. It was almost like when the rain came, and the earth opened itself to exchange water for its own special smell, the petrichor. I drank the water as quickly as I could, and some dribbled down my throat.

Bimbo said, 'Hey, Bub, don't waste it.' And I slowed my gulps to sips. He cupped his hands and drank as he lay facing the hole in the ground and then, twisting to look up at me, squinting through the glaring sun, he asked, 'So how many fish did you say?'

I giggled and sat cross-legged beside him and held up two fingers. The heat was already hot on my behind, but I wasn't going to miss this. Two fish from a hole in the ground? How could it be? But cool water had come from this place so perhaps fish could as well.

Bimbo lay face down on the ground again and dropped his shoulder, so his arm disappeared into the hole. His face was turned sideways towards me, and he shook his head very slightly, warning me to stay still, to be quiet. And as I watched, with the heat from the ground steaming my backside and the smell of the water making me think rain was coming, his mouth twitched and slowly pulled into a lopsided smile. Unhurriedly he rolled onto his side and, as his arm came out of the hole, I bent forward to get a better look.

He lay on the ground shaking with laughter at the look on my face. I had seen him do amazing things but never this kind of truly *big*, amazing thing. There in his hand lay a perch with its tiny orange-brown flecks and its rounded gills working like pistons searching for water in the air.

It was the size of fish we often caught and ate from the Georgina. I couldn't believe such a thing was possible. He tossed me the fish and, too hungry now to miss it, I clutched it securely and he turned back to the hole.

I ran and dropped each fish on a bit of hessian in the floor pan of the Land Rover and each time returned to the fishing place in that arid country.

Our fish gathered, I watched as Bimbo carefully moved the rock back over the hole. It immediately disappeared, blending back into its dry surroundings, and the petrichor faded into a heat haze. He broke a small branch from a nearby tree and brushed at the ground where we had been, and our marks, too, were gone back into the memory of earth. It was as if we hadn't had a cool drink of almost fresh rainwater and we didn't have five fish wrapped in a bit of hessian but, now in the vehicle, at my feet, was the evidence that such things had happened. Arid had become friends with water.

I was still too much in awe and couldn't ask any questions as we sat in the vehicle and Bimbo drove off further up the track. He glanced at me several times and grinned, probably because it wasn't often that I was lost for words. I was never a chatterer, but I constantly asked questions of Bimbo, who never seemed to tire of answering them. We got to the small clump of gidgea, drove off the road further into the wooded scrub and parked beside a tree. He got out and again looked around, watching the road for any signs of dust.

'Come on, Bub,' he said, 'let's have dinner.'

I jumped out and started to collect fallen twigs and small branches; we wouldn't need much. Gidgea was a great producer of heat and too much would burn our fish to a crisp.

'Why didn't we cook our fish back there?' My head and my mouth were full of so many questions and there seemed to be a race for them to burst out, but other questions were still brewing in my head too, pushing for space. They felt big.

'Too hot back there.' The words came with a look that was as ancient and still as those rocks that lay across the landscape. It was the look I got when there was more to a story. I knew that I had to find where those rocks were sitting and who they were sitting with. I knew I had to find my place with those rocks.

'Still hot here but I s'pose there's shade.'

'Yep, shade. Shade is good. Your nanna won't growl at me if we sit in the shade.' It was true. Nanna never let me out of the house without a hat, long pants and long sleeves. She expected we would keep out of the sun as much as possible and Bimbo would be sleeping in the shed if he did otherwise. Maybe it was another hangover from her Scottish ancestors. I certainly don't know but I stayed out of the sun and wore my hat 'cause Nanna said I must.

'Why are you watching the road? Are we waiting for someone?'

He laughed, dragged a match against the inside of the match tin and watched it, cupped in his hands, flaring into flame. He crouched to the pile of twigs and lit the fire. Stepping away, he told me to watch the fire and make sure it burned down okay and that he had to go and check a dingo trap we'd set the previous day. We always had traps set; I had several of my own that were only ever used when I was out at Herbert Vale with Nanna and Bimbo.

He said he'd be back by the time the fish had cooked so I had to put them into the coals when the fire was ready and, with that, off he went. I watched him until he disappeared with the trees and in that time the fire had changed from a collection of burning twigs to a collection of coals. I used a long thin twig to spread the coals and carefully placed the fish on top, then made little heaped coal mounds over them. The fish soon started to sizzle in the coals with little spits of juice making noises and having arguments with the fire.

I got the billy out of the Land Rover and carefully filled it from the waterbag that hung on its carrier on the bullbar and pushed it into the coals near the fish. Some cautiously positioned twigs on the other side of the billy soon had the water boiling. A small handful of tea leaves tossed in on the boil and the water soon became the deep golden colour that Bimbo liked his tea to be. I placed our tuckerbag on an old piece of calico I'd spread in the best shade and sat down. It was a still day with little breeze and so the flies started to chase around my face. I flapped them away and lay back, gazing up into the gidgea spread above me. I loved gidgea. I thought it wondrous. That was another word I'd read in one of my schoolbooks recently and it seemed to be exactly right for gidgea. These words I kept reading in books intrigued me and made all kinds of possibilities sit in my head. It was scary what the words could do.

Angry yellow

I recalled the school play that year, when I was about nine, which made me angry, so I slapped a fly that was crawling towards the fruitcake box. It left an ugly yellow splatter on my hand, which I wiped on the deep rough bark of the tree. After looking to see if Bimbo was returning, I took a mug and poured some water from the waterbag into it and, balancing the mug just so, I slowly dribbled the water into my hands and washed them. I hated yellow fly guts. I really didn't like most yellow things and my memories of *that* school play still made me wild.

The yellow dress was such a beautiful princess dress and, if I'd wanted to be a princess, I'd have loved being measured for it. My Aunty Sylvia gave one of her dresses to Mum to adjust its fit for me. I had to be in the school play. Just like when I was in Year 1 and Mrs Finch made me be in the play. Like it was my fault, back then in Year 1, that

Chrissie wanted the swing when I was already on it, and it wasn't my fault that she couldn't fight and didn't duck in time to miss my punch. Luckily, I didn't punch her too hard – the punishment hurt us much more than my punch had hurt my best mate. We both had to be fairies that time, wearing crepe-paper skirts and tops, singing about red and purple and pink and green rainbows ... It still makes me ill but that time, at least, I wasn't alone because Chrissie was in it too. That time we were punished together.

I was in Year 5 this time, Chrissie was gone – her dad, a drover, had gone over Charters Towers way with a mob of cattle so all the family had left – and the new teacher at Camooweal school was talking about Shakespeare with the high school kids. They had rewritten a story, which they planned would be a play to be performed at the end of the year in the town hall. There was a range of characters but none of the high school kids wanted to be the princess, so they made me do it. I was tall and played hockey in a mixed squad of high schoolers, and even though I was the goalie, they did bully me at times, so I was the princess.

'You only have to say three words, Debbie ... twice. That's just six words and that's it. You're done. You just stand there then ... and look faint. Six words, faint,' they all told me. My mum, of course, rather liked the idea of her daughter being a princess in the local school production and said, 'Yes, of course I will make Debra a dress.'

I don't know why they thought I needed to be told the

sum of three words times two. When I was in Camooweal and at school, the teacher would often give me the lower classes to teach while he took those older kids, probably to write that absurd play. I knew my maths and I'd read about fainting in a book, so I knew what that was as well. I had to practise looking faint because it wasn't something that I was, but no problems really. However, the three words presented a very big problem.

'Oh, deary me,' flutter the fan, 'oh, deary me,' flutter the fan ... look faint. That was all I had to say and do. But what a disaster. I could read the words but couldn't pronounce them correctly. My accent was strongly Wakaja and the words that came from my mouth, while sounding a little strange in English, meant something completely different in Wakaja language. I stood on the stage in the town hall – it was one of the few times that Aboriginal people were allowed inside and didn't need to peer through the slatted doors – in my beautiful yellow princess dress and said in my Wakaja-accented English, 'Oh, duri me. Oh, duri me.'

Neither my mother nor my father was prepared for their very school-clever nine-year-old daughter to stand in front of the entire town and say, 'Oh fuck me, oh fuck me', while fluttering a fan and looking awkwardly faint. The only saving grace was that the non-Aboriginal people had no idea what I'd said. They sat and clapped the little brown girl standing on stage in a pretty yellow dress. *They* didn't notice that the Aboriginal people had a moment of awkward quiet before clapping, with the women looking aghast and the kids snickering. Serve my mum right for making me be a princess! And my team knew why I let the two goals pass into the net the next time we went into Mount Isa to play hockey.

The smell of cooked fish roused me from my memories and I saw Bimbo heading back. I pulled the billy off the fire and carefully lifted the fish from the ash and placed them on an old tin plate from the tuckerbag.

'Nice feed, Bub,' he said as he sat down to eat. He had come around the vehicle and stopped to wash his hands from the canteen on the back and some of the soapsuds were still draining from his hands. There was some blood on his shirt and on his boots, so I guessed we'd caught a dingo and he'd already skinned it. And, when I sniffed the air, I could smell faint dingo.

He poured his tea, and we ate in silence, each with our own thoughts. Mine ran back to the fish and the water and the rock in the arid land.

'How did you know about the water, Bimbo?'

After a considered silence, he told me. It was a place that the Kalkadoon sometimes travelled through, and they always stopped there. They would travel from Lawn Hill way, from that place called Boodjamulla. He said, when he was a little boy with his uncles, they walked through here, and this was the only good water for a long way.

'Why did you walk this way?'

'You remember the stories I told you? We were travelling for those, but other people come for this water. Other people who are travelling through this country.' I turned this over in my head and recalled the many stories Bimbo had told me. I saw that he was not going to say any more about the travelling and I was glad. It was not a story for speaking of openly, so I turned back to my other questions.

'Why is the rock over the hole?'

He said it was to keep the water safe. If the rock covered the water, animals wouldn't fall in and they knew where to find water anyway. Covered, the water would stay fresh and it wouldn't dry out in the heat. And then he stopped and we both listened to the silence. It was as if he waited for a signal to continue to talk. The trees seemed to still and the buzz of the flies that had managed to track us here faded. Gidgea and earth stopped to listen; flies and the ants listened.

When Bimbo started speaking again, he took a deep breath and said, 'If we tell *them* it is here, they will dig it up for the cattle. If that happens, there will be no water left for the people, no water for this country. You are not to tell anyone about where this water is, Bub. Tell no one about this rock here. No one.'

And with those words he looked me in the eyes, and there by the burned-down gidgea coals and a carefully stacked pile of cooked fish remains, I understood this was the most important thing I would learn that day. Protect the water so it can take care of the people and the people will care for the country. I knew then the reason he looked so often for dust and the reason we hid the marks of our visit to the water. I also knew why we travelled into the gidgea scrub to make a fire and cook our fish. We each looked at the other and both faces broke into half-smiles because, even at that age, I understood the sorrow in those words.

'Well, what about the fish, Bimbo?' This was my attempt to change the mood.

And with that he tossed his head back and laughed his beautiful laugh with his shoulders and crossed legs all shaking. Bimbo always laughed and he often broke into dance, and this looked like a sitting dance of utter happiness. His face reworked itself and he laughed not just through sound but through his whole body. The joyous sound floated up into the gidgea to be taken into its leaves and I breathed too, to keep the joy.

'Let's bury these bones first and then I'll tell you how to do it.'

So we dug a hole and laid in the dried yellow bones of the fish. After covering them and placing a rock on top so the dingos wouldn't dig them up, he showed me, as we sat in the shadows cast by the gidgea trees, how, with my hands, I could take fish from cold water in arid places.

Moving place

Soda left by foot and travelled to the south. He knew that the manager would be after him as soon as it was discovered he was gone. With luck, they would think that he had gone to the north-east with his mother. He travelled most of the day, following the dry creek beds and staying below the line of the grass. The old people knew he had gone, and they knew which way he was going. It would have been useless not to tell them. They could read the dirt and the grass quicker than the crows find death.

The plain stretched as far as the eye could see. No trees and no water, but Soda had learned to travel in the ways of the old people. He could cover the imposing distance of the plain and never leave a trace that any of the manager's men could see. They would need one of his own people to track him and he knew he would always be under the protection of Old Paddy. The new occupiers didn't know how to travel in this country. They needed to scar this place, making marks to find their way. Soda didn't need to mark this country and scar it; he could travel day or night without hurting that which gave him life. He travelled with this country.

He had learned many things since he had gone through the ceremonies. He was sad they were not the ceremonies of the Gudanji, but the Wakaja ceremonies were now his. This country had grown him and so, through the ceremonies, he had become Wakaja, even though it was Gudanji blood that had made him.

As the plain stretched further still, he looked for the change of colour in the dirt. It signalled where he had to turn more to the east. If he continued two days' walk, he would be close to an outstation where he knew some people and, another day after that, the border into Queensland.

Towards the end of that first day, he came upon a small pool of water. It was a strange colour, and the smell wasn't what it should have been. The waterhole had been poisoned. There was a fence around it to keep stock from wandering in to drink. A little further on, under a large rough rock and surrounded by dry desert and gravel country, was a watercourse that wound its way underground. Soda had been shown its hiding place during the initiation time. It was a place that the old people had used and was part of the stories that mapped this country. Soda approached the watercourse carefully because it wasn't completely hidden but, if he was lucky, he wouldn't be the only thing looking for water at this time of the afternoon and he might be able to get something to eat.

He lay on his stomach on the ground, across the flat stone covering the water, and curled his arm down and under its ledge. He drank what he needed, then pushed his hand down again, to the bottom of the shallow water, and spread his fingers wide. He curved his fingers into an open, clawed hand and then he waited. It wasn't long until he felt the brush of something in the water. Don't move, he told himself. Soon, but wait first. There it was again, the touch of the fins of the small fish that were always here. At the next touch he grasped the fish quickly around the gills.

He took only four of them. He needed to eat but lightly. Soda carried the fish into the dry bed of gravel, which may have been a river bed at some time in the past, and made a small fire. He chose a place with care so the glow of the coals would not be seen at any distance or by anyone who might be looking. He then took a small clump of long dry grass, returned to the flat rock and brushed away any marks in the dirt made by his feet or his body. The old people would know he had been there but no one else would know. After he finished eating, he buried the bones of the fish and the coals of the fire deep in the sand. He then perched himself in one of the old spreading gidgea trees that grew further along the dry gravel waterway. If he'd had more time or had got to the creek earlier, he could have found a better place to sleep but here, in the dense scrub that cast dark shadows, would be safe enough.

The next morning, he lowered himself from the tree and continued the walk to the east. He could see across the patches of plain to the treeline in the distance, where the gidgea started to change to snappy gums and coolabah. He was still deep in the country of the Wakaja people and just a bit further was the country of the Waanyi. He had no reason to think they would be hostile. They also were facing problems with their lands being overrun by the four-legged beasts and being claimed by the marndaji.

As he walked, Soda was able to gather small amounts of the food that was often collected by the women in his family. The magurridi and muralama were both good to eat. Magurridi were small brown fruits, round and rough on the outside, with a hard white centre. Sometimes they contained a small amount of water that was really tasty and quenched the thirst. Muralama were tiny crunchy balls of white crisp flesh inside a soft green mottled skin. They also had a lot of water in them and were often eaten by his people when out hunting on the plain for long periods.

Near the end of the day, he could hear faint thuds in the distance and, as he stood with both feet firmly on the ground, he felt the same sound coming through his soles. He knew that was the sound of horses. If he got to the scrub, he might have a chance; out on the plain he had none. He started to run in a controlled jog. He knew he could run at that pace for as long as he needed, and he had a feeling he might have to for some time. Soda jogged on, repeatedly looking back over his shoulder to see where the horses were. At last, he caught sight of them far off to the north. His pursuers were at an angle that suggested they were guessing at the direction he was travelling in. He bent low and continued to move as quickly as possible.

He was very close to the gidgea scrub when the first of the shots rang out. Trying to stay hidden was useless now and costing him time. He ran. More shots rang out, but it seemed he was out of their rifle range. The scrub was just ahead now. The thick dark trees seemed to beckon and urge him to break into a faster sprint. More shots were fired and then the smell of gidgea came to him, giving him a burst of energy. The smell was always a welcome one, a pungent odour that mixed with the dust of the red earth as he slipped into the dense scrub. To those who were now approaching fast on horseback, it appeared that the trees had swallowed him.

Soda quickly ran into the deeper part of the scrub, where he knew the trees were particularly stunted and grew close to the ground. Horses would have trouble passing through these parts and the riders would probably have to dismount. He would have more of a chance if everyone was on foot and not just him. As he heard the shouts of the trailing posse and shots ceased, he watched from his hiding place. The manager and his sons and the offsider made up the group. As he made to move, a hand settled on his shoulder and another closed over his mouth. Old John grinned down at him with laughter in his eyes. *Gotcha,* he seemed to be saying. He silently motioned to be still.

The manager yelled from some distance away. 'Where the hell are you, John? Any sign of him yet?'

'No boss, nothing,' replied Old John, still with the huge grin across his face. Winking at Soda, he yelled, 'He's a clever little bastard, that one.' 'Teach him myself,' he whispered to Soda. Old John had guided him into manhood and taught him many of the skills for tracking and living in the bush. John was Paddy's younger brother so Soda had grown up calling him little dad. And if the Methodist minister came when Paddy was away, it would be his little dad who hid him.

The others in the group could be heard thrashing through the scrub further ahead. They made so much noise that the country closed down and held to its old-time secrets and laws, making their din loud and harsh across the landscape.

Old John bent down and spoke quietly into Soda's ear. 'You go through that turpentine and then over to that crooked tree back out that side of the plain. Camp there tonight. They won't burn this place now, the grass too good for their cattle so you be okay. In the morning go to the river and follow it all the way down. I will take them up that other way as far as I can. They might wake up and then we'll come back by afternoon next day, I reckon, so go quick.' With those final words, Old John walked away to follow the noise of the others.

Soda went and found the bent-over tree near the plain. He knew that Old John would keep them to the farthest side of the scrub, so he slept well. When he woke, the light was barely visible across to the east. The emu in the sky was slowly sliding away down the horizon towards where he was travelling today. As he got up, he noticed a small bundle near his feet. John again, thought Soda. Inside the bundle was another shirt, a small-bladed knife, a chunk of damper and a pair of shoes Soda had only seen before during the secret men's ceremony. He had never touched them before in his life and wasn't really keen to start now. The soft feathers were bound together with hair string to make pockets for the feet to slip into. When they were on, the wearer left no marks. He bundled it all back up again and hurried off, keeping his face towards the place where the sun would rise. He reached the river before sunup and, so he wouldn't leave tracks, collected some of the paperbark sheets falling from the trees. He placed them into a stack on the water and sat on it. With a long stick for a paddle, he was able to heed John's direction to go fast, floating down parts of the river. He ate the damper and drank the handy water as he travelled.

The landscape was changing now. He was passing through the open woodland on the edge of the plain country. The trees and shrubs grew between rocks and stones. Some of the stones were large and hid small caves. He could see only small distances in front and behind him because there were low hills and gullies. There was another station fairly close to these woodlands.

He had been floating again and now aimed his makeshift canoe at the bank and got off on a rock on the opposite side to which he had entered the water, a place where he knew his wet footprints would soon dry away, invisible to *them*. As he walked into the woodlands, he gathered the berries and plums that grew mad on the banks of the river. He made his way into a small cave and sat down. He was starting to get hungry for meat. Soda walked back to the entrance of the cave and lay on his stomach, watching for movement outside. Perhaps he would see a goanna.

Dust and mud

As the time passed and Soda's thoughts drifted, he mulled over what had happened and wondered what and where his mother was now. He hoped desperately she would stay with the drover and never return to that station, but he knew that neither place was good. Her choices were both dire – a drover's boy or a special girl. The same, just in different clothes.

He had asked his little mother, Jemima, about the whispers that night and she had finally told him the truth of it. The sisters had been locked in the back room of the station homestead and rarely allowed to leave it to sleep elsewhere. They had been expected to work in the house during the day and weren't allowed to leave at night but had to sleep in the back room. Some said that they were special house girls and at the time he remembered thinking it was a good thing that his mother and his aunt were special.

But Soda learned that special was not always a good thing, because those girls had been expected to provide sexual relief for the station manager, and his visitors, whenever they felt in need of it. Soda's mother chose to run away rather than stay and be that kind of special.

As the sun slowly moved down behind the horizon and he saw no movement anywhere, Soda crawled out of his hiding place and moved back to the water's edge. He scanned the banks of the river for the most likely place to catch something to eat. Further downstream he saw a small creek break from the main river. There was barely any water in the creek, just some muddy puddles. He would walk along there to find something. He hadn't gone far when he saw a turtle catching the last of the day's warmth on a flat rock. The puddle that was under the rock was so small the turtle wouldn't be able to escape. Soda continued to walk carefully up the creek bed. He had to remember to walk softly on rocks and sticks in the sand. Otherwise it would be too easy for someone to see where he had been.

The turtle was caught. He cooked it in the cave after making sure the wood of the snappy gum was very dry. No smoke came from dry snappy gum if the fire was made right.

Looking at a turtle always made him smile. What a strange animal it was. Why would it want to provide the cooking pot for itself? His people were from the plains country and didn't really enjoy turtle in the way people from the coast did. He was fascinated by the way they tipped the turtles upside down to cook in the coals. It seemed to work well; the flesh was always smooth and tender. Long-necked or short-necked turtle, he couldn't taste the difference, but they could. It was just another food source to him right now, and not his preferred choice, but still he thanked the turtle and the old people.

After the meal, he disposed of the remains in the way he had been taught, returned to the river, but not the shell. This was buried in the cave and he said more words to the ancestors that would help the turtle to travel on to its rightful place in another time. Then Soda curled up on the floor of the cave and slept.

The morning came quickly, and he was soon away from the cave, still following the river. He walked along the bank now, thinking that he'd travelled far enough the previous day to have broken the trail of his tracks. He felt he had the time to appreciate the horizon as the new day came up. The red and the orange spread across the sky, then slowly started to break up and disappear in a haze of heat. The pattern was always the same. Light, glow, colour and then all gone like rainbows that couldn't decide how to behave. Sometimes the colours were more intense, especially when it was burn-off time, and sometimes they were paler. As he walked he noticed the tracks of animals coming and going from the water. He saw the food plants that were fruiting now and those that were coming into season. The small golden tan berries he picked would give him energy to continue his journey. They held honey inside the crisp shell and the seed was good to suck as he continued to walk. Another of Old John's survival lessons, he thought, as he walked through the tall grass. Old John had told him to keep a small stone or very hard seed in his mouth as he covered longer distances. The presence of the foreign body produced water in the mouth. It also kept his mouth closed so no extra moisture could be lost to the heat.

Soda kept to the treed edge of the scrub and woodlands. He could look out across the plain and see anything from the north. The trees were also providing him with shelter from the heat and a place to hide from seeing eyes. He placed and lifted each foot in a rhythm that echoed through his ears. Soon he realised that the thudding was getting louder. He immediately sank into the tall grass beside a tree and watched. Across the plain he saw the horses and their riders. They were travelling parallel to him, not coming to where he was. They did not know he was there. He would soon be at a boundary and they would turn back. The manager wouldn't want to leave the station to itself for too long. Soon Soda could continue his travelling in peace. He crouched and watched the direction the riders had taken. He saw Old John lift his hand and wave as if to the riders following him but Soda knew it was a message for him.

Keeping the story

Tableland people talked with their hands as often as they talked with their voices and, sometimes, the hands talked much more. It was about a whole lot of things. Keeping the air space free to be able to hear all the other stories was the best way to learn about this country. The old Tableland people frowned on those who made too much noise, filling the air with unimportant me-sounds. 'Continue around through the woodlands' was the message from Old John, and then he wheeled the group away from where Soda lay hidden in the tall grass.

The earth turned red in the afternoon light. His walk, the soft repetitive thud of his heels, continued to echo in his heartbeat. Walk softly upon the earth and the spirits would be kind. It was a memory that sat somewhere safe within his soul.

The border was over the next horizon, in the far

distance. He didn't know what would happen when he got there. At least, he'd be an unknown. He didn't know if the act that made it illegal for him to think of himself as a human existed in the other state. Soda knew only that he was leaving behind all that was familiar, and all that was most likely to cause his death.

He had to get through the desert place first. And if he hadn't followed the old track, he would be crossing it without water. He had been there before with his uncles when it was ceremony time and knew there was a place to get water – hidden under a rock in the middle of what looked like big desert country.

As he walked across the final plain, the long thin line that was the fence showing the border came into sight. The heat of the Tableland was intense. With each step sweat gathered at his forehead, as did the dust, and from swiping at flies and sweat, a blood-red smear covered his face. As he stepped through the fence, he took a moment to stop and look back towards his country. Then he walked away, not knowing if it would ever be possible to come home, the only sign of his being there a tiny drop of blood, from a scratch on the barbed wire, already curling into the soil.

Lawless

On and on Bungmaji and his family travelled. They were slowly realising that this was possibly their final goodbye to their country and to their family. Nothing was ever going to be the same. They sometimes caught the distant ringing of metal against rock, but they were able to stay out of its path. They visited family and shared meals and melted back into the woodland scrub as if they had never been. Their heels continued to beat against the earth as their hearts continued to beat within their bodies and the red of the dirt continued to rise as dust and attempt to hold them there. Their journey to the south-west had taken them many days and now they were reaching a place that was only vaguely familiar. Soon would come the time when final goodbyes were to be heard.

On several occasions, the ringing had come very close and Bungmaji and his family could see the makers of that awful sound. The others sat on great four-legged beasts that had considerable strength in their long legs. And the beasts wore, on their hooves, metal that struck the country hard and rang out a threat of the coming danger and horror. The sound was foreign in this country, strange for the earth to hear, and only now was it becoming familiar to irriyani. With each step the beasts took, the sound called out to them and each call was rejected by the earth to ricochet around until it was lost. 'You do not belong here,' cried the earth. 'Bardba, run away.' But the sound spoke back. 'Beware,' it said. 'Change is here.' 'Bardba, run away,' called the earth.

Irriyani hid in the bushes and slowly the sound continued on its journey away from those who silently watched. At those times, fear sat at their shoulders and watched too. Fear took long, deep, slow breaths and controlled the dangerous urge to run. And fear joined in the silent chant of the watchers: 'Bardba, bardba! Run away, run away!'

As the ringing sound from across the rim of the foothills died away, Bungmaji stopped and placed his son on the ground. He silently motioned for all his children to come closer and so they gathered around.

'We go to different places now. We must leave here.' He pointed to his two daughters. 'You go to your family in the plains country. The Wakaja are good people and they will help you. Don't return to this place – there is too much killing.' With that final direction, he helped his son once more onto his back and started the long walk to the country in the north-west.

With a final glance over their shoulders, the irriyani became two small and lonely groups. The two women went south, where they became Wakaja nayida. They lived with Wakaja and birthed children into Wakaja Country, so their children became Wakaja people with the Gudanji living still in their memories, but memories have a strange way of returning, when they live in the depths of Country.

Fractures

His limbs were arranged as if in rest. That my father was lying on the ground looking up at me was strange enough, that I had caused it was stranger still. I remembered he'd hit Mum and I'd had enough. I remembered I'd struck out instinctively with no plan or thought. I'd heard talk of people just *cracking* and I think that perhaps that's what had happened to me. I'd just cracked. As I stood over my father, I took an inventory of what it was that might have cracked and broken. My bones seemed to be still together; my body showed no evidence of blood. What had snapped? I tried to recall those just-past schoolyard conversations to try and find any explanation there but no, nothing. I'd just cracked, and I'd hit my father.

That he was on the ground was not due to any pugilistic mastery on my behalf. I was sure, and I still am, that it was simply a matter of the great shock that he'd sustained.

A woman, his daughter, had retaliated and struck him. I stood there thinking through the options that might be available to me. I could run. I was regional athletics champion. Few could catch me in any kind of race when I really put my mind to it, but I immediately took that off the list. My father was one of the few who were better sprinters than I was, so running would be a waste of time and energy that I was fast suspecting I would soon need.

Further evidence of my mental storm and crash soon came as my mouth opened and I screamed at him to get up. I screamed at him and told him to 'stand up and fight like a man'. So perhaps something in my head had cracked and the thing that was broken was my brain. Certainly, my common sense was gone.

'Stand up and fight like a man, you bastard.' The scream came again. I begged for the voice to stop. 'Shut your mouth and be quiet, you idiot.' I watched Dad as he propped himself up on bent elbows, shook his head and slowly looked around him. Had he ever seen the world from just that angle before? I didn't think so. As a young man, Dad had often been paid to perform exhibition bouts in the boxing tents – he was brilliant at sparring. I'd never seen him fight in the ring. I'd seen other things, though.

'Get up,' I said. 'Get up!' The scream had become shriller and more desperate.

'Shut up, you idiot, he's gonna kill you' came from somewhere inside my head and tried to gain purchase, but the fractured brain had no surface for it to hold onto and it slipped around. More words shot around in my head and thankfully, at last, could not make the journey from there to my mouth.

Then came another voice, one with its own horror and desperation. 'Both of you stop. Enough, stop it now.'

I blinked and slowly my eyes focused on Mum. She was deeply angry. I wondered how I could see. I felt the tears running down my face and I knew there was snot coming from my nose. I slowly became aware that I was shaking, and the trembling ran through my entire body. My brain told me this was adrenaline, this was the flight, fright or fight response, and I gained a semblance of comfort from that. Perhaps my brain hadn't really cracked. Perhaps it had just reached a point of saying, enough.

Dad slowly rolled onto his side and sat up, drawing his knees into his chest. He laid his head on his knees and stayed that way for a timespan I could never guess at, but it was long enough for both Mum and me to notice his shoulders shaking. We looked at each other: What was he doing? I remember wiping the back of my hand across my face to remove some of the tears and it came away sticky. Was he laughing? Was he going to get up, and then what? There'd be hell to pay, that was for sure.

We moved closer together, and then Mum asked tentatively, 'Soda?'

And from the crouched position Dad still occupied

on the dirt, we heard a primal cry rise that ran down our spines. The pain in that cry came from a place so deep and so dark that it caused the shining sunlight to tremble and dim. That voiced agony tried to turn back into the darkness, but it had been freed. It walked straight out of the horror we had all experienced in private but now it was there in front of us all. We shared that moment and we all saw it. As it came away from the darkness, we knew it had a place in our memory and had become a chain that linked us in a way beyond the love and the terror and the family.

'Soda?' Mum spoke again. 'Get up.' And this time there was no scream; this time the voice was calm, and the voice was firm. 'Get up, Soda. Come on. Get up, it's okay.' I heard fear come into her voice, but it was the fear of caring too much, not the fear of more hurt.

Dad stood and, as I caught a glimpse of his face, I saw that the tears still running down my face were also running down his. I could barely stand the sight of my father in such deep and growing-in-your-bones pain. His face was twisted, almost unrecognisable. His lips quivered, parts of his cheek twitched and still the tears ran. I needed to take myself to some other place. I couldn't witness or be the recipient of the waves of sorrow coming from him. I turned away.

Mum grabbed my wrist and held me there. It shocked me that she now seemed to be in control. She had taken charge of the strings that seemed to be the only things creating any movement for Dad and me. I turned back to look at Dad.

'I'm sorry,' he said, his voice soft. 'I am sorry.'

He looked down at his hand and seemed shocked to see the knife clutched there. He raised the knife and looked at it, slowly turning and twisting it, making it become more familiar to his eyes. Gradually, his eyes made sense of the knife and he remembered. Dad looked at me and then back to the knife.

'I'm sorry, Bub.' I knew he was apologising because he had tarnished a special memory of mine.

The knife was the one my great-grandfather and I had made together; in my head, it was always Bimbo's knife. We'd picked up a piece of steel on the side of the road coming in from Herbert Vale and talked about what we could make with it. I had worked the bellows on the forge as my great-grandfather heated the steel and repeatedly struck it with a hammer until it took on the shape of a knife. Once that was done, Bimbo showed me how to sharpen and polish the steel until it cut as sharply as it shone. Then we picked a piece of gidgea for the handle. It was a leftover piece from when he made me a tiny boomerang. That knife was special and there had been nothing but beauty and love and wonder wrapped around it. Now the wrapping was gone, and I saw a knife that was capable of wicked and obscene things.

Dad took a step towards me and I instinctively moved back. I needed the distance to be maintained. He took another step, this one slower, more measured, and he bent down to place the knife on the ground. I stepped back again. He looked at me and the tears slowed.

'I'm sorry, Bub, I'm so sorry. I don't mean to get so wild, but I do. They did awful things to us and sometimes I just get so wild and it takes me over. They did awful things to us. They treated their dogs and cattle better and it makes me so wild, but I shouldn't hurt you or your mum.'

I took another step back and shook my head. It was an attempt to clear some thinking space but at the same time I wanted to reject that apology. My beautiful memory was gone and in its place was a new awful one. A new memory of my father holding me captive against his body as he pressed Bimbo's knife against the flesh of my throat. An awful memory of my father telling me I wasn't his child – I was too cheeky. I couldn't be his child – my skin was the wrong colour. I didn't want to know about what *they* did to him.

I wasn't ready to accept his apology nor was I ready to listen. I didn't want to hear his pain or to acknowledge his trauma or sorrow. Mine was more valid; mine was happening now, not in some time past. Mum pulled at my arm, trying to give me a shake to make me see that he was sorry, but I didn't want to know. In my head at least, I took back my knife and cut the strings held by my mum. The strings she had created in the growing and nurturing of me within her body, strings she had attended and maintained for all of my life. She had taken his side. In my head, as the knife cut those strings, I planned that my mum would never again force me to accept an apology, to turn the other cheek, nor would my father ever again be able to hurt me with his untruths. I was so busy planning all this in my head that I almost didn't hear the one time my mum truly did rage.

'Of course, he's your father, Bub. He knows it and so do you. Now both of you stop with this. *I* have had enough. Do you hear? I have had enough.'

His violence took on a whole other level of honesty that, in some corner of my thinking, I could almost respect. I had so much trouble understanding how it was that Dad was on the ground but, as I recalled events that led to this moment, I saw there was a strange chain of preceding, seemingly random, occurrences. And it was these that made me stop to consider the regret and the sincerity and the horror that I had heard in his voice.

Outside our home he was always careful to remain separate from those who might want to fight. And, when we moved into Mount Isa for me go to high school, he demanded I go to that school and learn; he also made me go to karate lessons. He paid good money for me to learn a different way, a way that was unfamiliar to him, to defend myself. It didn't make a lot of sense, but I saw that Dad was trying to give me the opportunity to protect myself from the violence when he couldn't. He made me go to school to learn these new language and story ways that were pervading our country and to be able to defend myself physically.

I didn't pay too much heed to his telling me I wasn't his child. I knew it in my heart at that moment, without Mum telling us anything, because within me lived the same rage and the same anger. And when it raised its head and when it burst forth from that deep, dark place inside me, the awful wickedness and evil came out, just like my dad. I'd seen it as I hit my father and watched him fall flat on the bare cold dirt without feeling any shame or sorrow. But, as I had just learned from my dad, I hated the violence and was ashamed to have participated in it.

Cloud stories

The wind was blowing again and so I hung my head. The feeling it gave me was the same as the last time, and the time before that, and the time before that. Had it always been this way? It seemed so. I looked more fiercely at my feet and the wind played at my ears. What if I could just glance quickly towards the horizon – would that work? Perhaps not. The wind picked up and pulled at my hair and several strands caught on my earrings. The self-talk started – you know the kind. After a bit, I finally arrived at 'Stop being a coward, Debra. Where would you be if they'd been like this?'

As the hair whipped across my eyes, I looked to the sky. I already knew what would be there. It was always there when the wind blew like it was. Always. And yes, there it was. The thick long roll of cloud, sitting just as I'd expected. I watched it, with the greys swirling together, but I saw far beyond the formations and the colours of the Morning Glory, this phenomenon of the Gulf of Carpentaria. People often flew their paragliders up there, dreaming and free, but in total ignorance of the messages they were silently soaring through.

When I lifted my eyes, which wanted to stay exploring the skin that covered the bones of my feet, I saw people and places long gone. And the self-talk faded to be replaced by a sound that I no longer recognised as words but whose meaning, deep and ancient, I felt as much as I heard. It rose through my body, it echoed in my head. Was it blood knowing blood? Was it bone calling to bone?

I stood in silence for a time and, once again, hung my head, gazing at my feet but no longer interested in the skin and bone. It was my own sense of loss that brought the tears to my eyes. My own sense of not being ready. Death was a strange thing. It shouldn't ever be a surprise, should it? No one ever seems to be ready or prepared for death but it's another step in the journey, yes?

We may need to return, I thought. We'd packed up camp at Little River and were making the trip back to the Sunshine Coast. Rick and I both watched the rolling cloud. When I looked carefully, I could imagine a hint of a face there, in those colours and shapes, and I knew who it was. We'd visited him before we left town to deliver the turkey we'd got for him. I should have been more prepared for this because, as we were leaving town, that turkey stood proudly by the side of the road as if in sacrifice, and so we shot it and took it to Uncle. I was happy that, thanks to our random act of stopping and taking that turkey, we'd had that last visit and food sharing.

Visions

We'd just come back from turkey hunting. We'd managed to get two, one each for Rick and my cousin. We'd been laughing so much during the hunt that it was amazing we got any. I was always complaining about sitting in the back of the troopie. They always said I should sit in the front but, if you sat in the front, you were expected to shoot and I refused to touch a gun unless it was completely, life-threateningly necessary. But, even as an adult, I was still too curious to be left behind so, as always, I just climbed into the back. The three of us had left the kids with their granny and off we'd headed.

In the back of the troopie, I held on for dear life, not because of speed but rather the rough country we were driving through. The track was cut up with now-dried wheel ruts where people had gone through mud during the Wet. We all bounced around as we wove our way on and off the track, according to no real logic other than feelings about where we would prefer to be if we were turkeys, where our heads and hearts led us.

The rifle lay on the rubber matting that covered the floor of the troopie and my foot on its butt kept it from moving too much. I didn't trust guns; the less I had to touch them the happier I was.

The vehicle came to a sudden stop, and we all held a little more tightly to our anchor points. My cousin and I watched the turkey off in the scrub as it walked with its beak pointing skyward. It watched us too and turned its head this way and that to see what we might do. I quickly took up the rifle and passed it through to my cousin, as he simultaneously reached back for it. I placed several bullets in his open-palmed hand through the gap in the seats.

'Where is it?' Rick asked.

'Ssshhh, see over there.' My chin barely moved to motion the rest of the sentence, but Rick missed that as well. He twisted around in his seat and my cousin and I both whispered, 'Ssshhh.'

'Can you see it there, Rick?' I asked while my cousin loaded the rifle and slowly positioned it.

Rick swivelled his head, looking around, trying to find the turkey. I didn't understand why he was having trouble seeing it — it seemed to be standing out like the proverbial sore thumb near a clump of long grass. I watched the gun now raised to a shoulder and braced myself for the noise to come. In my head, I told the turkey, 'Thank you for providing my family with food.' I told the turkey how much my children would appreciate eating the flesh from its legs and that the strength from those legs would live in my children's legs. And, as the gun exploded, I told the turkey how the grannies would eat the stew to make them feel strong and healthy. I told my grandmother, 'Thank you for bringing that turkey for us.' Lastly, I thanked the turkey for journeying to this place so we could find it and give our family its strength.

The explosion left a stark silence and we all sat for a moment as we saw the turkey drop to the ground. 'Poor thing,' my cousin and I both murmured. Rick hopped out of the vehicle and walked over to collect the corpse.

'How come he can't see them turkeys?' my cousin asked.

'Don't know. Can't work that one out.'

'You'll have to teach him to see ...'

Days later, Rick and I went out looking for turkeys. He was happy to have the chance to bring food home for the family. Rifle propped against my leg, bullets in their box beside me on the front seat, we drove off the track here and there.

Up ahead, I saw the turkey standing over near a woollybutt tree and said to Rick, 'This is close enough, don't you think?'

'What for?' he asked.

'Ssshhh ... to shoot the turkey.'

'What turkey?' But, fortunately, the vehicle had drawn to a stop.

'Can you see it there?' I was careful not to move because the bird was standing less than fifty metres ahead of the troopie, but my chin motioned and because I knew he still struggled to see things in the bush, I also pursed my mouth in the direction of the turkey.

We sat motionless for some time and then Rick said, 'Oh, there it is. Pass the rifle and I'll shoot it. I didn't see it there in the shade.'

He collected the turkey and, with the carcass in the back, we drove off, having decided we'd get one more for the old people who lived near our camp. As we travelled, I asked about how he saw things in the bush, how he looked at the landscape. It seemed a good opportunity to teach him to see.

'I see the trees and the grass,' he told me.

'And what about the shadows?' I asked.

'I look past the shadows because the shadows mess me up a bit and there's nothing there. I have trouble looking at the shadows because everything is the same colour and nothing stands out,' he said.

Rick and I shared a relationship with water. Gudanji come from the hills and the freshwater country, and our *big* story is about those three Water-women coming from the ocean. Rick was born on the Gold Coast, raised as a surfer. So I asked him about the rips in the ocean that he knew so well, how he knew where the danger in that water was lurking, and he explained that he just saw the rips — it was impossible not to see them. I reminded him that his relationship with the ocean was built through knowledge passed on to him from his father and then through his being *in* and *with* the water. Rick is an excellent waterman and he had taught our children to surf as they had started to find their feet on the earth. Strangely, I had taught them to swim — strange because I am not a competent swimmer at all. I had been taught how to teach swimming while I was at teachers' college, so a small part of my extended understanding of this liquid thing that runs through our fingers but pulls you into itself is theoretical, but Rick truly *lived* it.

As our children grew and learned to walk with country, they also learned how to be with water through the relationships Rick and I had and continue to have with such places. Our family's stories were separated by ancient knowledge, but they were both of the water. I asked Rick how he had taught the kids to see the rips in the ocean and finally he understood what I was trying to make him see.

'Okay, but how do you see turkeys?' he asked.

I told him about quilters and how they squinted their eyes to see different tones and shades in the fabric. It was an example that was familiar to Rick in a cultural sense. When I had learned to quilt and struggled to match colours and patterns, I was told to squint to see the colours differently.

But I never needed to squint because I grew on country looking for turkeys and goannas and I could always see them. It is the beginning of a way to see beyond.

We swapped over the driving then and as I drove along with Rick squinting his eyes to see the shadows, I narrated what he was looking for, what he should be seeing.

'Is it all shadow now?'

'Can you turn the colours really low, so the greens turn grey?'

'Now look for patterns. What can you see when you look for patterns?'

He saw random patches of shade now, so I asked if he could group them according to what he knew the scrub and woodland to be made of. Did he recognise the woollybutt and the bloodwood? Did he see the different tones they each cast? And so on it went until he could see that the bloodwood and its shadow were one, that the tree told us some of the story and the shadow told us some more. It never told us all of the story, though, so we needed to remember with our seeing. We talked about looking *through* the shade and learning the shapes of all the things in those places we drove past. And we talked about what to expect, what trees are growing partners and how they sit beside each other. Finally, I told Rick to look for the lines hidden in the shade because, to see country, you have to find the lines that run through everything.

I continued to talk Rick into some Gudanji memory.

Remember when we went that way with Mimi Peggy, and she told us about what the old people did there? See that big rock — do you remember what it looks like from that other side and the story for that place? And don't you think this place looks a bit like where we cut that sugarbag, where the parrots live? Draw lines between them all and remember the stories from each place and bring the knowledge and the relationships all together now with mankujba.

I told Rick to blur the stories. That is what Gudanji do when we are in the bush, on Country, at home — we blur our vision, without the squinting, to see the stories in shadows because we know that the turkey stands in between but so, too, might the goanna.

Rick has been learning to read through blending and blurring shadows for some years now and he knows that the mark-making of shade tell the stories in between. He is much better at seeing turkeys, though the turkey often waits for him, and sometimes he finds the sugarbag bees or hears the strange noises in the wind. Rick often feels that we don't ever walk alone on our country, but even after nearly forty years, he still struggles to feel all the stories. That's okay, though, because he didn't grow here on Gudanji/Wakaja Country.

Our children and their grandmothers are still teaching him things, so his reading is becoming better. Mimi Katie has taught him, like she taught her other sons, how to find the big barramundi and how to spear them. And she showed him what other foods are good to eat and where to find them, in and out of the water. And our children remember how their father taught them new stories about the ocean, so they teach him old stories about their Country.

Memories and messages

'Alalangmi nga mardumbarranka,' said Thungu, and she remembered what her Mimi Katie had taught her. This is her story, recounting that time she hunted for crocodiles.

* * *

Mimi knew about this crocodile business because she used to hunt them in a dugout canoe when the white people were still new to our place. She knew about the crocodiles and where they sat. When I was little, I sat with her, and she told me. When I was grown I worked at a crocodile farm and I was out gathering crocodile eggs in a swamp not so far from Darwin, just a short helicopter ride away.

I'm not as tall as many Gudanji or Wakaja women, so when I walked through the water, it was above my waist. I brought the air into my body to know this place and started to talk some more. I silently called to my old people and to the old people of this swampy place. I told them all who I was and why I was here. I asked that they help me be respectful in this place and I asked that the crocodiles walk with me too. Soon, I caught a thread of something, not a taste or touch or even a glimpse, neither smell nor sound. Just a tiny fleeting thread of something... and I knew I was not here alone. I listened more carefully with everything I am.

As I continued to wade through the water, which was muddy because the female crocodiles had been building nests, my eyes watched for movement that hadn't been caused by my cautious steps, or the steps of my two colleagues behind me. That strange sense of not being alone stayed with me. I talked again to this place and its old people, telling them that I was coming here to get some crocodile eggs for these marndaji where I work. Again, I told them who I am and where my country is, where I am from. I asked that they help me walk through their country today, that I mean no harm.

Nearly laughing at the thought of not being alone, because of course I wasn't, I concentrated on where I was. Looking around, I noticed the big trees that looked like the ones at Garranjini, but I was in this swamp near Kakadu, to the east of Darwin, wading through deep water renowned for its big angry mumma crocodiles. Who in their right mind made choices to do this stuff? I allowed myself a slight smile because I couldn't imagine being anywhere else at this moment.

Into my head came the voice that is often with me. My Mimi told me, 'Oi, be quiet and listen. Think about where you walking. You don't know this country ... listen properly. Did you see that little bit of paperbark over on the water's edge move? It's okay, just splash from that twig falling in. Watch those birds over there, up high. They can see good. Hang onto that oar good way, my girl.'

Lifting the boat oar off my shoulder, I adjusted my hold. The water was muddy but not enough to make the oar handle slippery – something to be glad about. In my mind, I ran through imagining how the oar would feel should I need to swing it. Carefully I measured its weight and again I adjusted my hold. There was a naturalness now about my grip on the heavy piece of shaped wood propped against my shoulder; it felt comfortable. I imagined it becoming an extension of my arm. Lift the weight and flick, like a ngalega because Gudanji have used spear throwers for a very long time.

As I continued to wade – the water was too deep for me to call it walking – I thought about the two others behind me. I was grateful they were keeping a good space between us all. John had warned Dave to stay about three paces, but not five, behind. It was all about the balance. Three paces were safe, five paces too much and safety went somewhere else. Yes, balance was good. We couldn't allow the crocodile an opportunity that a crocodile truly should never be given.

Mimi again asked, 'Did you see that bubble over by that big tree? Watch that bubble. Good girl, keep your eye on that little bit of water jumping near that black stump. See them birds ... they starting to feel no good.'

Slowly, our wading took us further from the helicopter drop-off point to the mound of decomposing leaves and tree debris. The wind curled around me in heavy breaths and then, on an almost not-there wisp of wind, came the smell.

'Did you smell that?' I asked the two behind me.

'Yeah, it's all pretty rotten,' came Dave's reply but I felt a nod from John that was accompanied by his low 'mmm'.

With each step, and more frequently on the wind, the smell invaded and became my focus in that place of composting vegetation and muddy water and lurking crocodiles. I could feel the mud sucking at my feet and I felt, rather than saw, the birds lift in flight from their perch at the top of the paperbark. And then I waited.

Mimi warned me, 'Don't step there. Just wait first. Watch now and hold that stick good way. You'll see that first ripple soon 'cause that smell is there in your nose. Stay still now, good girl. Don't put your foot that way.'

I stood waiting for the ripple. The two behind me waited.

'What's wrong? You okay?' asked John.

I liked John; he said he trusted me and my decisions. He

told me he had been doing this long enough to know that instincts were the thing that got you out of this place alive. He also knew where my mob came from, knew I had been taught deep-seated and ancient ways of knowing that came from long living with crocodiles. John knew my uncle and he called my family the salt of the earth.

I didn't move, just tipped my head, so he knew I was watching something. He stood still and I felt him turn to tell Dave to stop moving. Everything around us seemed to still and settle as if we had all drawn in a deep breath ... to wait.

'I don't think we should go this way,' I breathed back at him. 'We need to go around.'

Mimi told me, 'Good girl, yes. That's right. Go that 'nother way ... but watch for that ripple. It's gonna come soon. Get ready to hit that water. Wait first, watch now.'

Dave, who normally worked with the Riot Squad, looked across the open span of swamp water between him and the crocodile nest. He saw the carefully piled rotting vegetation in an unimpeded line directly in front of them. His day job had some of the highest burnout rates of any profession and the chance to volunteer for this seemed a good idea. A once-in-a-lifetime experience that he could add to, and tick off, his bucket list. The aim was to get to the nest and collect the eggs that would be buried carefully in the composting heap. Straight ahead. Twenty, maybe twenty-five, paces.

'What's the hold-up?' he asked. 'Around what?'

He missed the first ripple that barely registered on the surface of the water. And anyway, if you didn't know where to look and weren't looking for the bubble and if you didn't see the water barely jumping by the stump, the ripple was nowhere to be seen.

I stepped back a pace and pushed the oar into the water, gauging the lay of the swamp floor. When I was satisfied that the ground where we stood was relatively flat, I motioned John to come a little closer.

'I'm gonna hit the water now.'

John pulled his oar from his shoulder and adjusted his stance. 'Okay, I'm ready,' he replied.

And as the acrid smell of dead fish grew around me again and as the birds shrieked when the last of them flew off to find a safer perch, I watched for the tiny ripple to make itself seen. When the page of paperbark let loose its last grasp on its trunk, the ripple appeared and the boat oar, now raised high above my head, came crashing down onto the muddy surface of the swamp water. The ripple shattered and the middle of a huge splash of water became the crocodile, which had been lying in the belly of the swamp. The crocodile launched itself in a crashing explosion of water that caused the birds to turn sharply in their flight. And the water heaved as the crocodile sank back into the depths of the swamp with the crushed remains of a splintered boat oar clamped in its mighty jaws. The trail of muddy water left a dark wavy streak as the crocodile swam away from us where we stood in various degrees of astonishment.

After the violence, everything became still and quiet. Birds settled at their new roost and the minute ripple of water smoothed itself into the flat muddy surface of the swamp. The only evidence now that anything out of the ordinary had happened was the growing brown trail of stained water making its way across the swamp, clearly showing us the path of the retreating crocodile. Tiny clumps of grass and dirt littered the surface of the water and then slowly sank, while fragments and splinters of oar floated up from the depths, shattered like the peace of that place.

Mimi said, 'Wait for it first now. Let it sit down again quiet. Watch that water. Walk soft, my girl. Now, go.'

Holding the remains of my oar towards Dave, I smiled and said, 'We needed to go around that but it's okay. We go straight now.'

Making kin with Country

'Mimi tied barnmarrarna around my head,' said Lhudi, my
elder daughter, 'to keep the feather in place as we got ready
to dance.' It was festival time at Borroloola and all the
people were getting ready. My daughter, granddaughter and
I had journeyed from Darwin, for them to dance with the
Gudanji women. This is an account, from her perspective,
of one time that my daughter and my granddaughter
danced at Borroloola.

* * *

The Gudanji families had the best singer of all the clan
groups. Mimi E's voice wasn't just a sound that filled a
space. Her voice echoed in a way that seemed to be many
voices joined together singing the same but sounding all
different. Maybe all the Gudanji singers from the past were

singing through her too. Her voice was almost physical in the way it surrounded you and touched you from your skin through your ears to your heart. If you listened carefully and let the sound go inside, it almost led you through the dances. Her voice could show you how to dance because it filled you up inside, starting from your feet. It made time fade and twist and dissolve into the earth. When Mimi E sang, our country was the only thing holding us because her voice travelled through everything and took us all with it.

The sun was setting now and already the air, like us, was stained by the red dust. It made little halos as it played with the streetlamps that lit the dance ground. Like the insects that plagued the light, dust motes floated around and, if you looked carefully, some were already dancing. Cars continued to arrive, and all the Borroloola families set up their places on the edges of the dance ground. This was Yanyuwa Country so, by a long-held unspoken rule, or maybe just ordinary respect, the best vantage spot was left for their elders. Some families sat further back near the few scattered trees, and they lit small fires where they sat and waited for blackened billies to boil. They were some of the Gudanji families who didn't live in town, but remotely. They sat silently and they greeted the local elders like our old people did – with nods and head gestures, unobtrusive, silent but speaking glances and slight hand movements. Finger talk was good at times like these.

Dancing started and the Yanyuwa mob welcomed us all with their dances. Their red costumes looked good with the sun shining its last light, and I could hear my Mimi singing with the Yanyuwa songs. The Mara people came on next. They are from the north of Borroloola and are close with the Arnhem Land people. I enjoyed watching the Mara mob: they danced with lots of energy. Their headdresses are plaited and woven from black, red and yellow wool. My brothers jumped and twisted. The Garawa people, wearing blue, replaced the Mara dances. Their country is to the east, out towards the Northern Territory and Queensland border, but we are all family together at Borroloola.

I could still hear Mimi singing but she wasn't yet using her best voice. She was saving it for when she sang for our mob. Soon, it was the Gudanji's turn for dancing. We wore yellow and we all had a white feather tucked into our barnmarrarna. I checked again if my barnmarrarna was tied securely around my head and that my hair was held tight. As I gathered my dance board, I looked at the painting on it — fresh and bright with a yellow background. Mimi Peggy made new ones for the senior women, so I gave my old one to my daughter. She has been dancing with all the Gudanji women dancers for a few years now.

I have been dancing with the senior women for a while now too, not because of my age but because I am the oldest daughter of the oldest daughter. My mum is the oldest granddaughter of one of our important past elders.

Mum's Mimi passed on a long time ago now and Mum is her oldest living female descendant. It's important because our clan are from the Mararabana Dreaming and women are big bosses for that one. A long time ago, Mum's granny painted marks in caves that we have visited, and my sister and brother have that mark tattooed on their arm, the same as I do.

All our old people had been waiting for this, so they gathered families around. They told our little ones to sit quietly, and silence fell. We took our place on the centre of the dance ground and Mimi Peggy made sure she was happy with the way everyone was positioned. She took her time with this. Gudanji are a small group of people. There are stories telling of a big massacre in the 1920s when many Gudanji were killed, when small groups escaped and travelled to other places to be safe. We still haven't really recovered. I'm not even sure if that is something we can recover from. I feel something cut into my soul when I think about what happened at that time. There is so much pain just under the skin, sitting in so many places inside my body. When we dance, that horror fades a little and it hurts a little less. I think that when I dance, I maybe help the old people come back to our country.

The sound of clap sticks swelled and swirled up and around all of us in that place. Like the dust that had not yet settled from the previous dancers, the sound felt as if it came from the earth beneath our feet. It moved with the dust, mingling and merging until it was almost the earth calling the dancers to order.

Stillness settled over everyone as we readied ourselves for the dancing. And then Mimi E's voice travelled from a place we imagined through our bodies. I closed my eyes and felt the sound with my feet. It came from under the soles of my feet, and it came through my skin until it settled in some place inside that I didn't know existed until I started dancing with my family. It sat in the same place I felt the losses of Gudanji people from long ago, through causes both natural and obscenely unnatural, and where I know that I am enough because I am exactly as my ancestors have made me. I trust them implicitly.

It wasn't hard to imagine I was not just at the festival grounds at Borroloola but also in many other places too. It seemed I had left there and travelled back and forward and even through – way back to when feet had first walked on this country and a long way forward to when I had contributed to the dust that settled around the feet of Gudanji now as we danced. Way back to when the voices had only existed in the soundless space of open country. Mimi E's voice travelled with me or maybe I travelled with her voice; time became something else and so perhaps I did too.

I went way back to before this country felt the stomping that had created its heartbeat. I imagined feet striking the ground, becoming more than a whisper in this place.

I imagined the many feet stomping had become one with my heartbeat and so my stomping in that ceremony added my place to the long line of dancers before me from that first ceremony at Garranjini. All those women stomping heartbeats into our country, celebrating and birthing life, on and on.

I know that the essence of who I am, my kujiga, and where I belong, come from the shadows and whispers that I see and hear and feel when I am on country. I don't know who the authors of those whispers are, but I hear them, and they call to me in ways that are clear and loud and safe. I feel them calling for my feet to move to a rhythm that is deep inside my bones, but that I see when I am looking at our place, feeling the breeze or eating the fish we have been given. I know, too, that at some stage in the future, perhaps in the time of my great-grandchildren, or theirs, the shadows and whispers will speak to them, calling them to dance so they can link the stomping of their feet with the ancestors' stomping, and they can add their own feet into the heartbeat of our country. I know that, just as I dance with my long-past grannies, at some time in the future my grandchildren will dance with me.

We all danced until it was time to sit and let Mimi E's voice rest, while we sat with our memories and became entwined in our country's rhythms. Smells of beef cooking on coals mixed with the singing and the rising dust as we all ate the food our place has provided. And we gave thanks, always we talked to the old people, this Country.

The fires soon all burned out to leave blackened circles with billycan prints and a few tossed teabags burning away to char. People packed and left to return to where they all now lived. Us Gudanji mob live all over, but we always come home to ourselves.

* * *

After the dancing, my mob are going out to camp at Little River for a while. And we will sit by a fire and cook barramundi in the coals and talk about when we were young. Mum will want to remind us to remember and to listen so we will know, so one day she won't be the one saying, 'When I was little, my mum and dad told me ...'

Mum and Dad have spent much of their time travelling back and forth from the Sunshine Coast in Queensland to our place in the Northern Territory, typically spending several years at either place. They have done that so we could live with our Country as Gudanji people and learn who we are and where we're from. We grew up fishing and living out bush, gathering food, listening ... and walking with the stories. Our Mimis would also be with us; we are so lucky to have Mimi Katie and her big sister, Mimi Peggy. They are the best aunties and grannies we could have had to teach us who we are. They love going bush onto Country, getting out of town to teach us our ways, Gudanji ways, and Garrawa ways too for their mum, and Mimi Katie trusts Dad to take us bush by himself since she taught him everything.

Mum said that when we were little and Dad was new to our place, Mimi Katie would travel with us all the time. Mum says it's because she was worried that Dad didn't know this country. Mum often told Dad we had to stay home, in the camp, every so often so Mimi could rest but she has taught Dad lots now and he has lived with Gudanji for nearly forty years, so she trusts him to keep us safe now and to know that this country is more than earth, more than just us. Mimi trusts him to know this place now and to know that we have to walk softly.

When we set up camp at Little River, not so far from Garranjini, rolling out swags next to the creek, we made the fire bigger than usual. It has been a while since we were all together, so it is a fire to light the joy of being together and to celebrate. Maybe, too, the fire means all our kin, the human and non-human, can see that we are there and country is warmed with us.

Mum and my daughter are already by the fire, sitting on the spread tarp, and I watch as Drisana picks up a stick to toss into the fire. While Mum mixes up some damper, Drisana wriggles her backside to move closer and tosses the twig into the flames. She leans forward to pick up another and Mum, not looking up from her damper mixing, says,

'Don't even think it,' and Drisana drops the twig with a sad look at her grandma. 'You know what will happen if you play with fire at night, Nana?'

'No Grandma, what will happen?'

'You will goomboo in your swag. Then you and Mummy and Daddy will be all wet.'

'Hahaha, no, Grandma. I won't do that. I go to the toilet. I'm big.'

'My nanna told me that, when I was little, and she never told me fibs so you will wet the bed if you play with fire at night. Come here and help me with this damper now, please.'

And as I leave my daughter with Mum, my sister and brother help Dad unpack and I listen for Mum's voice to float across the camp and be taken into the leaves hanging above us. She will soon start to talk us back into being in this place, to remember the stories that wait for us, that welcome us home.

Drisana is now lying on her back, stretched across the tarp, looking skyward. 'Look, Grandma, there's a plane flying over us. Is Mimi fishing at the crossing right now?' she asks, remembering a plane flying high above us the last time we sat at the crossing at Borroloola fishing with her Mimi Katie.

Mum tells her that Mimi isn't fishing right now. Mimi has gone into Darwin but soon she will be back and, yes, she will be fishing at the crossing and the kids will look up at the sky and see shiny planes flying high over the top of everyone.

And so, to reassure her, Mum tells Drisana a story about the crossing and when Mimi's son was the ranger and he put a swimming cage in the river for the kids. All the families had been worried someone was going to be taken by a crocodile 'cause all the kids would swim in the river. The cage was really good because everyone could climb up the steel mesh sides and jump into the deeper water as well as climb up the stairs. One day we went to the river for the kids to swim in the cage and there was a crocodile inside it. We didn't know a crocodile could climb up the stairs of the cage the same way we did. Mimi Dickie took the cage away and there was no more swimming, but some kids still swim when they think no one is watching.

The business of feet

It was at the end of the Wet and we decided it was time to go fishing. Water and roads had dried out and the heat was gentle so off we went. As the troopie stopped, nearly all the kids jumped out and ran to the waterline. Grandmother made her way to her spot and sat with kids all around her. As I stepped out of the troopie with tarps and water, I saw that Jabanbi was still in the back of the troopie rummaging through the tuckerbox.

'You not fishing then?' I asked.

'Just want something to eat first, Mum. I'm hungry.'

'We just had breakfast, mate. Maybe you need some time for the food to hit your belly, eh?'

'Nuh, I'm hungry.'

'How about a drink of water? Maybe you need some water to wash your breakfast down.'

'Nuh, I'm not thirsty, I'm hungry.'

'Well, there are sandwiches in the box.'

'Nuh, don't like tomato.'

'There are cheese sandwiches in there.'

'Nuh, don't want cheese.'

'There's fruit. Maybe an apple or an orange will be okay?'

'Nuh, I want food, Mum. I'm hungry ...'

'Well, I only have sandwiches or fruit. If you're that hungry, the river is there. Maybe you need to go catch a fish!'

He gave me a look that spoke of frustration and of being close to running out of patience, then he turned away. The conversation was over, apparently. He jumped out of the back door of the vehicle and walked to the collection of fishing gear sitting in the shade of a nearby tree. I turned to the river, leaving him riffling through the stack of handlines tumbling from a fishing bag. He was five years old and it was rare that I had to deal with a tantrum from him. He was almost the perfect child. He arrived on his due date, he ate what I gave him and he slept when I told him to. He played with his sisters, and he wasn't loud or nasty or brattish. He very rarely made demands of any kind.

We would go out on country and he would listen respectfully, walk quietly and watch carefully, and he was already more than competent at living well in the bush. He lived humbly through the generosity of country and the wisdom of the old people.

He would come around any moment now, I thought. Some of the other kids were sitting at the river with a fishing line but most were playing behind us, running between the trees and ant beds. I knew Jabanbi would soon be running around with them. He never sulked either.

I sat and tossed out my line.

Sometime later, I noticed that he still wasn't with the kids playing and I carefully looked around. Everyone was still fishing or looking now for sugarbag in the open country behind us. No one had called out to say that Jabanbi was going with them, so he had to be somewhere close.

I looked over to my sister and she glanced towards me, lifting her chin as she did. 'What's the matter?'

I twisted my hand back at her and said, 'Jabanbi.'

Her chin pointed to the other side of the troopie.

I got up to take a better look and I could smell woodsmoke — someone had lit a fire. I followed the smell away from the water to a stand of paperbark trees on the other side of the troopie. The fire was mostly burned out now but a few ends of burning snappy gum lingered, and it was all circled by a ring of carefully placed stones. Sitting at the stone boundary was Jabanbi.

It hadn't been a large fire and now there was a billycan of water fenced in by more snappy gum pieces slowly growing from ember to flame. Two cooked black bream rested on some paperbark near the fire. It was the fresh soft inner paperbark we used for food. It was moist and didn't flake into dusty bits. If we used it for cooking, it gave a subtle flavour that was like sipping clean scented air. The fish were cooked to expose the white flesh through the crisp charcoaled skin.

'What are you doing?' I asked.

'I just cooked my fish 'cause I was hungry.'

'And so where did you get the fish? Did Mimi give them to you?'

'No, I caught them with my line.'

'Oh?'

'Well, I was hungry, and you said to catch a fish. Do you want some?'

'Thank you … yes, please.'

He carried the two black bream down to the riverbank and sat on a flat rock. I brought some water from the troopie and sat beside him. After we'd dusted our fish with some salt, I passed him a bottle of water. We sat there for a while, watching the river and eating the fish. We wondered aloud together if anyone had found sugarbag and hoped they had. Brushing away a few stray ants, he started to remove his shoes.

'Don't take your shoes off, mate. There are too many bindi-eyes.'

'It's okay, Mum. My feet need to breathe and stretch for a bit. I'll put them back on soon.'

'What do you mean breathe and stretch for a bit? You'll get sore feet if you don't put your shoes back on.'

My son looked at me with aged sadness in his eyes. And, for a moment, I wasn't sure who I was looking at or talking with. He turned his head at an angle I had seen my own father use when seeking how to explain something deep. When he raised his head, my father's eyes looked at me through the face of my son. I saw the knowledge of many lived lives and profound experience.

'Mum, my feet know this place. They just need to get out of the shoes. You know they've grown here. They've walked everywhere here on this country. If I let them out of the shoes for a bit, they'll be happy, and they'll be able to breathe.'

He paused and gazed at the rock walls of the gorge across the river from where we sat. He looked up towards the place where the Mermaid women sang and danced and made our place way back in the Dreaming. I knew he was noticing the sounds of the wind as it moved through the soaring rock walls and the way the birds gathered at a particular place on the river for water. I knew, too, that he saw the way the rock walls had been shaped by the water that continued to rush through and carve out a path for its journey back to the sea. I didn't know what else he was seeing but his gaze seemed to focus now on some halfway place, neither here nor there.

'You know they are not my feet.'

'Then whose feet are they, mate?' My tone was curious.

'Well, I'm borrowing them, Mum. They belong here to

this place because this is where they've walked for a long, long time. This is where they've grown. The bindi-eyes don't matter. My feet have felt all those things here before. They've walked with my grandfather and your grandfather and lots of grandfathers before us mob. They know this place. These feet that don't belong to me have grown here.'

Being

Fifteen years later and, once again, we were on Country. This time we had a group of non-Aboriginal people travelling with us. They were friends and a few other people I'd met through work. They had all decided they wanted to spend time on Country, the way our family does, a real experience in an ever-evolving moment, not a tourist event. We had swags and fishing lines. Our tuckerbox was minimal, though it did have a French press and freshly ground coffee.

We had driven the nine hours from Darwin along progressively quieter roads and, by the time we arrived at our turn-off, we had passed a mere three cars in the preceding four hours. We had an hour to go and there would be no cars now. We were, at last, in our place. The dust rose from behind the four-wheel drives and windows were securely closed. Air conditioners were turned up and people held tighter to seat belts and hand straps until at last we could stop. We were at our camp.

Everyone got out of the vehicles with relief and regained some of the energy that had stilled during the long drive. Camp was established and the fire built and, yes, the coffee plunger was whipped out and sat, along with all of us, awaiting the billy boil.

Gratefully sipping hot coffee, people peered around at a landscape that was new, and significantly intimidating. We all watched as the sun moved lower in the sky. It was that peaceful quiet time of the afternoon when the birds were around and, until their chirping truly moved into your ears, it sounded noisy, but then their song blended with the brushing of foliage and the symphony happened. Jabanbi had gone down to the river and caught fish for dinner as soon as we arrived, so everyone had an early night in swags rolled out under the stars. With our bellies warmed by a feed of fish and woodfire smoke making fine lacy curtains filtering the stars, we watched the red flashing lights of the planes high above us and went to sleep.

We rose with the birds the next morning. There was excitement about the day ahead. The plan was that we would hike the five kilometres to Garranjini in the cool part of the day, wait out the heat and fish, walking back to camp in the cooler afternoon. We would catch our lunch and dinner. The walk would be broken up for morning break by more coffee and johnny cakes, to be cooked as we fished.

The camp was set up atop an escarpment. The view looked over the valley carved by the water flooding from Garrinjini since those three Water-women made that place in the Dreaming. The only way to get to the valley floor meant a rough, sixty-metre climb down. Rick had gone ahead to make sure any buffalos, wild horses or cattle were scared away and could be seen on the other side of the river. About halfway down, I realised I hadn't put in any matches to start a fire. I asked Jabanbi, only half in jest, if he wanted to make a fire with sticks. When he raised his eyebrows, I told him I'd left the matches behind. Nobody in our little group was a smoker so it was either a quick return for the matches or the undesirable stick fire making.

'I'll go back and get the matches. You all keep going. I'll catch you up,' Jabanbi said, and off he went, back up the rocky incline. The rest of us continued to pick our way down to the valley floor, being careful not to slip on loose rocks and dirt. Each step was marked with the noise of sliding rocks and hushed by the followed drift on dirt. After walking for about twenty minutes, we arrived at the edge of the river.

'We need to go just a bit further. There's a clear spot up there where we can all sit and fish for a while,' I assured everyone, and so we started off again. Several people wondered if we should wait for Jabanbi but were told that he would be fine, he would catch up with us and, no, he would definitely not get lost.

As we got closer to where we would sit and fish, I smelled campfire smoke. My daughters also noticed, and we all looked at one another, wondering who was around. Where was the smoke coming from? We were the only people here. The others were now also starting to smell the smoke. 'Is someone else camping here?' they asked.

The smell was close now and under the burning of wood was the aroma of cooking. It wasn't beef, it was fish, and as we rounded the last bend we came to the fire. It sat in a clear spot and several fish were cooking on coals. Jabanbi sat a little away from the fire with his fishing line in the water.

'What took you so long?' he grinned at us, pointing to the tugging line in his hand. 'This is my third fish.'

I grinned at him, hoping that my 'smarty pants' thought was obvious. Laughing, he took the fish from the line and then filled the billy from the river. The others were still looking at him strangely.

'How did you get here so quickly?'

'Did you pass us somewhere on the track?'

'We didn't see you. Did you really go back up to the top?'

Questions fired all around him. After placing the billy in the fire, he rearranged the wood to build the flames.

'This is my country,' he said in a quiet voice. 'I was grown here in this place and these feet have been travelling here for a long time. I just have to listen 'cause my feet, they know this country.'

Yarned into place

'Nyamirniji ilinga jaburru,' she said. 'You listen first and then you will know.' The road stretched ahead, an astonishing river of earth that we, travelling in a white troopie, moved along as if in a boat. As far ahead as we could see, the road continued straight. Someone had taken out a grader and dug a straight line across the landscape as easily as they would have used a ruler to draw a line on a paper map. And they built that road, so straight and flat that it ironed out all the history this country had lived and seen, leaving just that awful scarring mark. But, when we looked behind us, swirling and billowing waves of red dust obliterated the road, twisting and turning in eddies and breezes. There was not a straight line to be found anywhere.

'Long way now, Gourdi, or nothing?' I asked of the elder woman who was mother, aunty and grandmother to those of us in the vehicle. She sat in the front seat and gazed out along the road.

'Little bit more,' she said. 'Not long way.'

I glanced at the kids sitting in the back with me. The almost imperceptible dip of heads indicated they'd heard but no one commented. They, too, gazed out the window at the passing landscape.

I didn't really want to be one of those bratty kids asking, 'Are we there yet?' so I asked, 'Which way now, Gourdi?' And I looked ahead at the road. It was still as straight as it had been ten minutes ago, the last time I asked.

'Not far,' she said. 'We pull up around the next bend.' My aunt and I and the kids in the back all looked at one other and then looked again.

'Which bend?' the eyes asked.

'Where was the last bend?' the eye conversation continued.

'Gorn then, you ask her,' said the eyes. We broke eye contact and, rather than feel the disapproval coming back at us from the front seat, stared into the landscape distorted by glass, dust and passing movement. We laughed quietly among ourselves at our fear of her disapproval or disappointment. None of us had ever wanted to risk that.

Rick looked in the rear-vision mirror when the laughter broke out. He tipped his chin in the direction of the dash and I saw that the fuel indicator was close to three-quarters empty. I hadn't noticed where it was when we started so

I just shrugged my shoulders. The road was busy enough; someone would be along if we ran out of fuel.

Vegetation blurred into bands of green above the red dirt as we continued and eventually, up ahead, the road disappeared. We all sat straighter. There was a bend in the road! Ten minutes later and in the middle of the blurred orange-browns of the bloodwood trunks and the splashes of red from the leaves of the little grevilleas we used to dye the pandanus for our baskets, Gourdi said, 'All right, stop now.'

After directing Rick to stop just so, we piled out of the vehicle and stood on the side of the road. Looking around carefully, I tried to find a landmark, but there was no large rock or distinctive stand of trees that I could use. To my eyes, it looked the same as it had five minutes back down the road. And this was Garawa Country and so even more unknown to me. I handed bottles of water to the kids and tossed around hats that had been discarded during the drive.

As I pulled my hands from placing two oranges into my pockets, Gourdi looked at me and said, 'We walk this way now.' And so we did.

We walked for a long time after we lost sight of the vehicle. We walked and we walked, passing isolated clusters of cycads, some of which towered over our heads, through open forests of woollybutt. I gave up worrying about finding our way back to the troopie. Neither my granny nor my aunt would be lost here – after all it was their place, Garawa Country – and I could track us out if needs be. The children were still learning how to walk without their footsteps marking the earth. As the sun started to descend, we approached another cluster of cycads. Gourdi picked up pace and we strived to keep up with her eighty-year-old legs. Her soft murmuring cautioned us to continue slowly and, as we did, our feet walked more softly at that place. No dust needed here. Gourdi continued to murmur, and we started to hear the names of family being recounted. She stopped and so did we.

Fanning out around her, we looked at what seemed to be another circle of cycads. They ranged in size from less than thirty centimetres high to those that towered over our heads. Many were bent from the weight of the clustered fronds atop their two-metre trunks. Gourdi walked around the cluster, picking up nuts that had fallen in this recent burn-off.

Each nut she picked up was examined and considered carefully. She looked at the size and the shape. Her fingers ran over the surface and, if they found what she looked for, she passed it to her other hand. When the size and shape and texture were wrong, it was dropped back on the ground.

'Here now, you mob,' she said and passed into our hands several nuts each time. 'You put this one into this ground here now. Bury him into this ground. Like this ...' And with shuffled feet, she dug a shallow trench, then motioned for the closest grandchild to place the nuts in before shuffling feet covered the nuts with the powdered earth.

'What we do this for, Gourdi?' one of the little kids asked. Gourdi took the hands of the closest children and it seemed necessary that we all join hands. She walked us around the clustered cycads and wove us through them. Stopping occasionally at particular trees, she told her story.

'This one here' – gesturing to some of the smallest trees – 'I put with my grandmother. I was young girl. Only little one. That one, my mother put with her grandmother. That big one there, grandmother's grandmother put there when she was little one with her granny.'

As we stood in that place, Gourdi called the names of family before us who had lived their lives with this country and had stood at this place and shuffled cycad nuts into the earth. She reminded us all of the names of ancestors who shared our blood, and she talked us into that place, and into the earth. Names that linked us with our ancestors, which had been handed down from person to person, became part of the air in that place and left something of us all there after we left.

'You all put some in the ground and now we got more. Family, all us mob, we made this place.'

Returning song

Mararabana story time, the kids were all thinking. We all sat around a fire that cast only enough light to yellow a few of the trees that stood closest to where we sat. The faintest ribbons of smoke rose from the single gidgea log slowly letting itself burn into white powdery ash. I breathed the smells and caught the wet traces of damp coming from the river.

Children leaned against grannies and the adults sat with their mugs of tea dangling from fingers, arms resting on bent knees. The moon was slipping away to the west as the bones and charred skin of the turtles, the remains of our dinner, were intermittently fed into the fire.

Back in that Dreaming, before we came here, three women came in from that salt water, the ocean. They travelled over country going long way, for long time,

and they would sit down at some places. You know them
places. We call names for them in ceremony. You listen.
When you dance for this story, you feel this story.

Arm waving to the north-east of us. Gesturing with up-and-down strokes. Poking at the log with an extended leg. The disturbed ash flew away with the rising heat to settle where it would, taking with it the remnants of gidgea stories and sonorous voices. As the whispered sounds in the undergrowth mingled with the low-voiced words of our story, we imagined ourselves travelling through those faraway places. Imagined the first journey before we came to be Gudanji. And with the motioning of arms, the stories continued and with them, us, Gudanji, sitting at the fire traversing time and space through memory with and of our forebears and our Country.

They travelled down over that dry country. All the way
down past Elliott through that desert country and then over
near Tennant Creek. They were looking for this thing, like
this feeling, so they only sit down there for a little while.
Resting, you know. Then they travel again. Long time, long
way. Looking this way, looking that way.
    In that dry country, that big gidgea place, they
turned around then near that big hill there in the middle.
They turned around and started to come back up this
way, travelling, sometimes sitting down and sometimes

dancing, sometimes making fire. They was thinking about something, they was thinking about a feeling, they was thinking about that big water they came from. They was starting to get sorry feelings for that water where they came from. They was looking for that salt water. Mankujba way.

Smooth sweeping outstretched arms. Hands making short circular patterns and we imagined ourselves moving through the boulders of the south country. Fingers flicking and brushing against a smoothed fabric-covered leg, and we saw the plains country. Fingers flicking and brushing in the dust, making small eddies rise and settle onto skin, feelings and knowledge settled within us and like a splinter under fingernails we remembered the sorrow and pain of that journey. We remembered.

A sip of tea and the cups, here and there, placed on the ground and as we sat, we returned with the ash of the gidgea and the sleepy voices recalling and retelling that story rising and falling into the earth. Tea finished, so attention turned again to the listening.

They come all that way then across the Tablelands to this place. Gudanji place. They got here and they was too sad with that feeling so they sat down here, and they danced, and they had that big ceremony here in this place. Might be they carried that gidgea from down that dry country

*to this place. Might be they made a fire here too. But they
called up that water then, singing and dancing for that
water, and it came to them. It came to them because that
water knew that feeling and it was feeling sad too. Water
came over that rock. You see it? Washed away that rock
for this feeling, that water came washing that track for
itself. That water came here all the way. All the way to
this country.*

A tiny hand crept across Granny's leg and held a
hand that was old and gnarled with age. Granny moved
her hand and enclosed the little one. Two hands, one
wrinkled and scarred from all the storying it had told, all
the living it had done, and the other so smooth and soft,
having not yet experienced anything to add to this story.
The ancient journey was being slowly shifted from a hand
old and wise to a hand so young. With the child's hands
wrapped in hers, Granny continued her story. Her hands
now gestured in child size, making short circular patterns
together.

*Them three Mararabana, they found that feeling here
and so they was feeling happy again. Might be it was
feeling like home for them 'cause then they sat down,
and they sang some more, and they made this country.
Big ceremonies to make this place. All them animals and
trees and bushes and then us. Them three Water-women,*

they made us mob here in this country. We come with this place. This place made us, this fresh water and hill country.

Acknowledgements

Rick, there is neither time nor paper enough to tell you how much you bring to my life. The good days, and the not so good, are better with you.

To Lhudi, Thungu and Jabanbi, to my precious granddaughters, Drisana and Johnny, to San and Aaron, thank you for your patience and your amazing support during this thing that ate up so much of our family time. Thank you to my daughter, Ryhia, who did not once roll her eyes when I asked for 'just one more tiny change' to the wonderful artwork she created for the cover.

And thank you to my family at Mount Isa and Borroloola, particularly to my wonderful Gudanji and Garawa Elders, Katie Bandulurrga Baker and Peggy Yaburrnalina Mawson.

For the storytellers of my Gudanji and Wakaja family, including those non-human voices, thank you sharing with me those big learning ways that we have lived with and through since the very beginning, and for letting me create this work.

You all make my life a true privilege.

My deep and sincere gratitude to Dr Antonia Pont, my PhD supervisor, for her generosity and expert guidance in developing the thesis from which this book is drawn. I am forever appreciative of her integrity and her timely involvement in this journey, for sharing her knowledge, wisdom and the joy in academic rigour.

Thank you to Juliet Rogers and the team at Echo Publishing for their guidance in this process of book making.

Thank you also to two of Australia's most important writers, David Malouf, whose contribution to Australian literature is immense, and Dr Tyson Yunkaporta, a brilliant thinker, researcher and academic, for their kind support of my book

Lastly, I offer my heartfelt thanks to Deakin University for the scholarship that allowed me to spend time on Country developing the bones of this narrative and share those days with the ancestors and kin.